BSCS Science T.R.A.C.S.

An Elementary School Science Program

Investigating Position and Motion

Teacher's Edition
Level Two

BSCS

KENDALL/HUNT PUBLISHING COMPANY
4050 Westmark Drive   Dubuque, Iowa 52002

BSCS Development Team

Nancy M. Landes, Project Director and Author, 1996–98
Gail C. Foster, Author
Colleen K. Steurer, Author
Vonna G. Pinney, Executive Assistant
Linda K. Ward, Senior Executive Assistant
Rodger W. Bybee, Principal Investigator, 1994–95
Harold Pratt, Project Director, 1994–96
Janet Chatlain Girard, Art Coordinator, 1994–96

BSCS Administrative Staff

Timothy H. Goldsmith, Chair, Board of Directors
Joseph D. McInerney, Director
Michael J. Dougherty, Assistant Director
Lynda B. Micikas, Assistant Director
Larry Satkowiak, Chief Financial Officer

Contributors/Consultants

Randall K. Backe, BSCS, Colorado Springs, Colorado
Judy L. Capra, Wheatridge, Colorado, free-lance writer
Michael J. Dougherty, BSCS, Colorado Springs, Colorado
B. Ellen Friedman, San Diego, California
Cathy Griswold, Lyons, Oregon
David A. Hanych, BSCS, Colorado Springs, Colorado
Jay Hackett, Greeley, Colorado
Debra A. Hannigan, Colorado Springs, Colorado, contributing author
Karen Hollweg, Washington, DC
Winston King, Bridgetown, Barbados

Paul Kuerbis, Colorado Springs, Colorado
Donald E. Maxwell, BSCS, Colorado Springs, Colorado
Marge Melle, Littleton, Colorado, free-lance writer
Lynda B. Micikas, BSCS, Colorado Springs, Colorado
Jean P. Milani, BSCS, Colorado Springs, Colorado
Renee Mitchell, Lakewood, Colorado, free-lance writer
Brenda S. McCreight, Colorado Springs, Colorado, contributing author
Mary McMillan, Boulder, Colorado
Carol D. Prekker, Broomfield, Colorado, contributing author
Patricia J. Smith, Tucson, Arizona, contributing author
Terry Spencer, Monterey, California, contributing author
Patti M. Thorn, Austin, Texas, contributing author
Bonnie Turnbull, Monument, Colorado, free-lance writer
Terri B. Weber, Colorado Springs, Colorado
Carol A. Nelson Woller, Boulder, Colorado, contributing author

Field-Test Teachers and Coordinators, Levels 1-3

Joanne Allen, Grade 3, Westport Elementary School, Westport, Maine
Helene Auger, Westport School District, Westport, Maine
Sheila Dallas, Grade 2, Bethany School, Cincinnati, Ohio

ISBN 0-7872-2279-8

Any opinions, findings, conclusions, or recommendations expressed in this publication are those of the author(s) and do not necessarily reflect the views or imply the support of the National Research Council or the American Association for the Advancement of Science.

10 9 8 7 6 5 4 3 2

Pat Dobosenski, Grade 3, Pembroke Elementary School, Troy, Michigan

Nina Finkel, Grade 1, Whitter Elementary School, Chicago, Illinois

Mary Elizabeth France, Grade 2, Westport Elementary School, Westport, Maine

Carolyn Gardner, Grade 3, Calhan Elementary School, Calhan, Colorado

Shelly Gordon, Grade 2, Bingham Farms Elementary School, Birmingham, Michigan

Darlene Grunert, Birmingham Public Schools, Birmingham, Michigan

Terry Heinecke, Grade 1, Edgerton Elementary School, Kalispell, Montana

Katherine Hickey, Grade 1, Irving Primary School, Highland Park, New Jersey

Jan Himmelspach, Grade 1, Grayson Elementary School, Waterford, Michigan

Janet Smith-James, Grade 3, Bartle School, Highland Park, New Jersey

Elizabeth Lankes, Grade 3, Bethany School, Glendale, Ohio

Barbara O'Neal, Grade 1, Calhan Elementary School, Calhan, Colorado

Cheryl Pez, Grade 2, Bethany School, Cincinnati, Ohio

Rochelle Rubin, Waterford School District-IMC, Waterford, Michigan

Elizabeth A. Smith, Grade 3, Grayson Elementary School, Waterford, Michigan

Melanie W. Smith, Grade 2, Washington Elementary School, Raleigh, North Carolina

Catherine Snyder, Highland Park School District, Highland Park, New Jersey

Ingrid Snyder, Grade 1, Waterford Village School, Waterford, Michigan

Lee Ann Van Horn, Wake County Public School System, Raleigh, North Carolina

Kathy Wright, Calhan Elementary School, Calhan, Colorado

Reviewers, Levels 1-3

James P. Barufaldi, University of Texas, Austin, Texas

Larry W. Esposito, University of Colorado at Boulder, Boulder, Colorado

Brenda S. Evans, Department of Education, Raleigh, North Carolina

Randy Gray, National Weather Service, Pueblo, Colorado

Judith Johnson, University of Central Florida, Orlando, Florida

Eric Leonard, The Colorado College, Colorado Springs, Colorado

Brownie Linder, Northern Arizona University, Flagstaff, Arizona

Jerry Ludwig, Fox Lane High School, Bedford, New York

Mike Madsen, KKTV, Channel 11, Colorado Springs, Colorado

Kathleen Roth, Michigan State University, East Lansing, Michigan

Cherilynn A. Morrow, Space Science Institute, Boulder, Colorado

Barbara W. Saigo, Saiwood Biology Resources, Montgomery, Alabama

Gail Shroyer, Kansas State University, Manhattan, Kansas

Carol Snell, University of Central Florida, Orlando, Florida

Joseph Stepans, University of Wyoming, Laramie, Wyoming

Richard Storey, The Colorado College, Colorado Springs, Colorado

Joan Tephly, Marycrest University, Iowa City, Iowa

Jack Wheatley, North Carolina State University, Raleigh, North Carolina

Acknowledgments

Photo Credits

All photographs in the Teacher's Edition are by Carlye Calvin. The photographs that appear on the reduced facsimile pages are credited in the Student Guide. See the Acknowledgments page.

Art Credits

BSCS art files; Linn Trochim; Dave Blanchette

Design and Prepress

PC&F, Inc., Hudson, New Hampshire

Cover

Rollercoaster courtesy of Corel, Map image © 1997 PhotoDisc, Inc.

CONTENTS

Investigating Position and Motion

Preface

During the 1990s, American education entered an era of standards-based reform. Standards have been published at national, state, and local levels in almost all subject areas. With the release of the *Benchmarks for Science Literacy* by the American Association for the Advancement of Science (AAAS) in 1993 and the *National Science Education Standards* (NSES) by the National Research Council in 1996, the science education community joined this reform effort.

The intent of standards in science education is to define in a concise way what all students should know and be able to do to become scientifically literate citizens. Although many people are involved in defining and developing the standards they expect students to meet at national, state, and local levels, few have attempted to provide working models of what standards-based science education might look like in the classroom. *BSCS Science T.R.A.C.S.* provides such a model for the elementary school classroom.

In *BSCS Science T.R.A.C.S.*, students learn basic science concepts, as defined by the *NSES* and the AAAS *Benchmarks*. Students learn these concepts through engaging experiences that involve them both physically and mentally in the processes of scientific inquiry and technological design. Each module clearly defines the standards that students are to meet and provides a sequence of developmentally appropriate experiences that allow students to develop a true understanding of the concepts presented, not just a superficial overview of related vocabulary and facts.

BSCS Science T.R.A.C.S. includes everything the busy teacher needs to help students meet high standards, including complete lesson plans, well-defined assessment strategies, a structure for collaborative learning, an instructional model that connects the learning experiences, background information about the science content, and a How-To Handbook. The Handbook is full of practical suggestions for everything from establishing a safe and manageable learning environment to using journals as effective tools to promote learning to helping students construct their understanding of science concepts. The curriculum does not require teachers to have special laboratory facilities, equipment, or extensive background knowledge in science or technology.

To be successful, any curriculum program requires the skill and creativity of dedicated teachers who help students make sense of their learning experiences. BSCS welcomes feedback from users of this program so that we can continue our tradition of providing leadership in science education. If you have suggestions or comments, please direct them to: BSCS, Attn: *BSCS Science T.R.A.C.S.*, 5415 Mark Dabling Blvd., Colorado Springs, CO 80918.

With *Science T.R.A.C.S.,* BSCS continues to set the standard in science education. Thank you for your interest and support. We hope you and your students enjoy and learn from this exciting, innovative approach to elementary science education.

Timothy H. Goldsmith, Chair
BSCS Board of Directors

Joseph D. McInerney, Director

Introduction

Your Teacher's Edition begins with an abbreviated version of the Program Overview. In it, you will find the curriculum framework, the features of the program, and a brief introduction to the *National Science Education Standards* and the *Benchmarks for Science Literacy* that guided the development of the program. The complete Program Overview is located in the *Teacher's How-To Handbook* of *BSCS Science T.R.A.C.S.* Make sure that you read the complete Program Overview before you begin teaching this module. It contains directions, many helpful hints and the information you need to understand this inquiry-oriented, standards-based approach to elementary science education.

Doing Science	Doing Technology
Wonder	Wonder and identify a problem
Ask questions	Get ideas to solve the problem
Observe with your senses	Design something to solve the problem
Investigate	Build a model of the design
Use tools	Test the design
Record by writing and drawing	Make or build the design
Share your ideas	Share your ideas
Wonder and ask new questions	Wonder and identify new problems

BSCS Science T.R.A.C.S. was organized and designed for elementary school students and their teachers. In this program, students actively develop concepts, inquiry skills, and problem-solving skills by "doing science" and "doing technology" through a sequence of developmentally-appropriate activities.

Each module in this program

► engages students in the processes of scientific inquiry and technological design;

► allows them to explore objects, events, and organisms in their
environment;

► invites them to develop and explain concepts in their own words,
both orally and by writing and drawing;

► presents content information in a developmentally-appropriate and
engaging fashion;

► provides opportunities for students to extend and elaborate their
understanding and knowledge through independent inquiries; and

► includes performance assessment opportunities whereby the
students and teacher can assess students' progress in conceptual
development, inquiry skills, and collaborative work.

Curriculum Framework

Level	Physical Science	Earth & Space Science	Life Science	Science & Technology
K (TE Only)	Investigating My World			
1	Investigating Properties	Investigating Earth Materials	Investigating Animals and Their Needs	Testing Materials
2	Investigating Position and Motion	Investigating Weather	Investigating Plants	Designing Sound Systems
3	Investigating Electrical Systems	Investigating Objects in the Sky	Investigating Life Cycles	Designing Structures
4	Investigating Changing Properties	Investigating the Changing Earth	Investigating Ecosystems	Solving Pollution Problems
5	Investigating Heat and Changes in Materials	Investigating Weather Systems	Investigating Human Systems	Designing Environmental Solutions

What are the features of *BSCS Science T.R.A.C.S.*?

Standards-based   The *National Science Education Standards* (NSES) and *Benchmarks for Science Literacy* guided the development of the curriculum framework, the lesson outcomes, and the overall approach to teaching and learning found in *BSCS Science T.R.A.C.S.*

Research-based   The research on children's thinking and development of science concepts informed the outcomes and sequence of activities in each module.

For All Students   Hands-on science motivates all students to learn concepts and skills. All students can participate in the activities at their developmental level. The program provides team support and encourages independent investigations.

Constructing Understanding   The "5 Es" instructional model sequences the learning experiences for the students so that they can construct an understanding of concepts, not just recite and memorize information.

Active Learning   Students are actively involved both physically and mentally in doing science and technology. The program emphasizes high-interest, developmentally-appropriate activities that are related to students' lives.

Collaborative Learning   The structure for collaborative learning is built into the program. Through collaboration, students engage in dialogue and discourse that help them learn concepts and the inquiry skills involved in doing science and technology. It also provides a means for students to develop important social and management skills.

Assessing Understanding and Abilities   Instruction and assessment go hand-in-hand in *BSCS Science T.R.A.C.S.* Each lesson includes a variety of assessment strategies that involve students in demonstrating what they know and can do.

Equity   The activities and organization of the program encourage the active involvement of both girls and boys and are appropriate for students of all racial and ethnic backgrounds.

Student Guide   The program includes a student guide and resource book for students. The student guide is not a "read-about-science" book; rather, it serves as a guide to help students become more responsible for their own learning, both collaboratively and on their own.

Teacher's Edition   The Teacher's Edition is designed with the busy teacher in mind. It includes helpful preparation guidelines and detailed teaching and assessment strategies to help you organize and manage an activity- and conceptually-based science program. Facsimiles of the student pages are integrated throughout the manual just where you need them.

Kits of Hands-on Materials	Activities use simple, readily-available equipment that does not require elaborate storage or classroom space. The equipment and supplies are familiar to students and relevant to their lives and development levels.
	A kit of hands-on materials is available for each module. The kit contains those materials not readily available in the classroom or from students' homes. The kit includes order forms that facilitate taking inventories and reordering consumable materials.

What are the *National Science Education Standards* and the *Benchmarks for Science Literacy* upon which this program is based?

National Science Education Standards

The *National Science Education Standards* (hereafter referred to as the *Standards*) define the science content that all students should know and be able to do and provide guidelines for assessing the degree to which students have learned that content. The *Standards* detail the teaching strategies, professional development, and support necessary to deliver high quality science education to all students. The *Standards* also describe policies needed to bring coordination, consistency, and coherence to science education programs.

The vision of the *Standards* states that all students, regardless of age, gender, cultural or ethnic background, disabilities, aspirations, or interest and motivation in science, should have opportunities to attain high levels of scientific literacy. The guiding principles include:

- Science is for all students.
- Learning science is an active process.
- School science reflects traditions of contemporary science.
- Improving science is part of systemwide educational reform.

The *Standards* are based on the premise that learning science is something that students do, not something that is done to them. The *Standards* envision an active learning process in which students

- describe objects and events,
- ask questions,
- formulate explanations,
- test those explanations,
- communicate their ideas to others, and
- build critical and logical thinking skills.

Many people were involved in the process of developing the *Standards*, including teachers; science educators; scientists and engineers; publishers; those from informal science settings, such as museums and science centers; school board members; parents; and members of business and industry. The process was coordinated by the National Research Council (NRC), which is part of the National Academy of Sciences, the National Academy of Engineering, and the Institute of Medicine.

Benchmarks for Science Literacy

The *Benchmarks for Science Literacy* (hereafter referred to as *Benchmarks*), a publication released in 1993 by the American Association for the Advancement of Science (AAAS), specifies what all students should know or be able to do in science, mathematics, and technology by the end of grades 2, 5, 8, and 12. It is a companion report to *Science for All Americans* (SFAA), a document outlining science education reform that answered the question, "What should the substance and character of science, mathematics, and technology education be for today's children entering tomorrow's world?"

According to AAAS, the *Benchmarks* is different from a curriculum, a curriculum framework, or a plan for a curriculum. It is a tool to be used by educators in designing a curriculum that makes sense to them and meets the standards for science literacy recommended in *Science for All Americans*. SFAA presents a vision of science literacy goals for all students to reach by the time they finish the 12th grade. *Benchmarks* maps out the territory that students will have to traverse to get there. *Benchmarks* can be characterized, as follows:

- *Benchmarks* is a report from a cross-section of practicing educators.
- *Benchmarks* describes levels of understanding and ability that all students are expected to reach on the way to becoming science-literate.
- *Benchmarks* concentrates on a common core of learning.
- *Benchmarks* is informed by research into students' understanding and learning at specific age and grade levels.
- *Benchmarks* is a developing product.

The development of *Benchmarks* was a grass-roots effort, involving a substantial number of elementary-, middle-, and high-school teachers, school administrators, scientists, mathematicians, engineers, historians, and learning specialists. The effort was directed and supported by the Project 2061 staff of the AAAS.

How did the *National Science Education Standards* and *Benchmarks for Science Literacy* guide the development of *BSCS Science T.R.A.C.S.*?

The *Standards* and *Benchmarks* guided the authors of *BSCS Science T.R.A.C.S.* in developing the curriculum framework, the outcomes for each module, and the overall approach to teaching and learning for elementary school students and their teachers. Specifically, the documents

- helped the developers focus on the most important concepts and skills in science and technology designed for elementary school students;
- established boundaries for the scope of the curriculum;
- helped structure the framework for the sequence of concepts;
- clarified inquiry, teaching, and assessment strategies appropriate for elementary school students and teachers; and
- provided an important research base for determining the developmental appropriateness of specific concepts and skills.

The framework and outcomes of *BSCS Science T.R.A.C.S.* provide a well-researched, well-organized, developmentally-appropriate approach to addressing the *Standards* and *Benchmarks* and are designed to give students every opportunity to meet the standards established at the national level. As a result, the program will meet the majority of state and district guidelines if those guidelines are based, at least in part, on the *National Science Education Standards* and *Benchmarks for Science Literacy*. Because grade-level placement of topics and concepts will vary from state to state and school district to school district, this curriculum framework might not match local frameworks exactly, but the major concepts and skills will be addressed within the grade spans of kindergarten through grade 5.

Children and Science

> *If I had influence with the good fairy . . . I should ask that her gift to each child in the world would be a sense of wonder so indestructible that it would last throughout life, as an unfailing antidote against the boredom and disenchantments of later years, the sterile preoccupation with things that are artificial, the alienation from the sources of our strength.*
>
> Rachel Carson

The world in which we live is a wondrous place. It is full of nooks and crannies that invite exploration. It is full of curious creatures that invite observation. It is full of natural wonders and technological inventions that invite investigation. It is full of people, each of whom is unique and a biological marvel. Fortunately, some of those people are children who inspire a sense of wonder in us all.

Science is a natural endeavor for children. From the time they are born, the primary job of children is to find out about the world around them. That also is the job of science—to find out how the world works. Our job is to bring children and science together in a meaningful way so children do not lose their sense of wonder and curiosity as they develop a better understanding of the world around them.

Introduction to *Investigating Position and Motion*

A child's world is full of engaging objects to investigate and to think and talk about. Each of these objects takes up space and occupies a position. Many objects can change position as a result of motion. Children constantly observe and discuss these spatial relationships, and they express their ideas about position and motion in everyday terms.

> *I couldn't catch the ball because it was way over my head.*

> *My toy car rolled down the hill faster than yours did. It stopped farther down the hill, too.*

> *When I wound up the swing, I spun around really fast. Then, I went slower and slower until the swing finally stopped.*

> *The snake stayed still for a very long time. Then it crawled under that log and scrunched up by a rock.*

What Piaget calls "spatial concept" develops slowly over the years. Describing the position and motion of objects requires visualization and spatial thinking ability—the ability to visualize and manipulate images in the mind's eye. Visual/spatial skills are crucial to helping children understand how their world (and beyond) works. These skills are the mental constructs that allow students to visualize or make mental pictures of moving objects and to manipulate or rotate an object's position in space. Students' simple experiences with position and motion in this module provide the foundation for their future understanding of the movement of the earth around the sun, for example, or of the motion of molecules within a material when it is heated.

At the beginning of the module, students describe the position of objects. Although we can describe position only in relation to some other object, the observer often is unaware of using a reference object to describe position. Students at this level have an egocentric viewpoint of space. They naturally observe and describe the world relative to themselves rather than to other objects. These egocentric descriptions of position are usually too ambiguous to be accurate or to allow communication and comparison of ideas about objects in space. However, through a series of games and other activities, students realize that describing the direction and distance from a reference object provides more precise information about the position of an object.

After students are able to effectively describe an object's position, they begin to observe and describe an object's motion as it changes from one position to another. By experiencing activities in which they create yarn paths and ski trails, investigate the motion of a rubber ball, and race drops of liquid, students

- refine their observation and communication skills;

- recognize that objects move in many different ways, and describe the motion with such terms as straight, zigzag, round and round, back and forth, and fast and slow;

- understand that they can describe position and motion;

- develop their ability to describe position and motion effectively and accurately, and

- develop their visual and spatial thinking abilities.

In addition to enabling students to construct their understanding of position and motion, the lessons in this module are designed to provide primary students with the following

- hands-on, minds-on learning experiences

- critical thinking and inquiry skills

- a conceptually-developed, coherent sequence of experiences

- a need to develop communication skills through the four Rs—record, reflect, report, and read—all in the motivating context of science

- opportunities to learn collaboratively with other students

- integrated activities that encourage curiosity and imagination

See the *Module at a Glance* for a summary of the lessons and the development of the concept of position and motion.

Module Outcomes

Conceptual Outcomes

Students' experiences throughout this module help them develop an understanding that each object has a position and that a change in an object's position is a result of motion of the object. Students understand that they can describe accurately an object's position as well as its motion.

The following table illustrates the priority placed on conceptual development in the module and also displays the correlation of the module's conceptual outcomes with the *National Science Education Content Standards (NSES)* and the *Benchmarks for Science Literacy*.

Module Outcomes	Related Content Standards (NSES) and Benchmarks
Concepts Developed	
The position and motion of an object can be described accurately.	Describing things as accurately as possible is important in science because it enables people to compare their observations with those of others. (Benchmarks, Scientific Inquiry, K-2)
An object's position can be described only by locating it relative to another object.	The position of an object can be described by locating it relative to another object or the background. (NSES, Physical Science, Position and Motion of Objects, K-4)
Objects move in many different ways.	Things move in many different ways, such as straight, zigzag, round and round, back and forth, and fast and slow. (Benchmarks, Motion, K-2)

Module Outcomes	Related Content Standards (NSES) and Benchmarks
Concepts Developed	
An object's motion can be described by tracing its position over time. An object's motion can be described by measuring its position over time.	An object's motion can be described by tracing and measuring its position over time. (NSES, Physical Science, Position and Motion of Objects, K-4)
Concepts Addressed	
Pushes and pulls change the motion of an object.	The position and motion of objects can be changed by pushing or pulling. The size of the change is related to the strenght of the push or pull. (NSES), Physical Science, Position and Motion of Objects, K-4)

For further information about how this program is organized to enhance conceptual development, see *How To Help Students Construct Their Understanding of Science Concepts* in the How-To Handbook.

Scientific Inquiry Outcomes

The module also places primary emphasis on scientific inquiry, involving students in both structured inquiry and independent inquiry. We have divided the inquiry outcomes into two types: those that help students develop the **abilities** necessary to do scientific inquiry, and those related to students' development of **understandings** about scientific inquiry. The outcomes chart at the beginning of each lesson indicates which abilities and understandings that lesson emphasizes.

See *How to Involve Students in Scientific Inquiry and Technological Design* in the How-To Handbook for a complete listing of the Science as Inquiry Content Standards from the *National Science Education Standards* and the related benchmarks from *Benchmarks for Science Literacy*.

Collaborative Outcomes

The primary collaborative skill developed in this module is **Ask for help and give help.** The first few lessons in the module reinforce the basic collaborative skills introduced in previous grade levels. Students should continue to apply those skills whenever they work in collaborative teams.

Teaching, reinforcing, monitoring, and processing the collaborative skills are essential if students are to work effectively together. We recommend that you review thoroughly the opening lesson, *Doing Science,* which introduces the team skills in the student guide. Continue to monitor and process the students' use of all the skills throughout the module.

For information about managing collaborative teams and developing collaborative skills, see *How To Create a Collaborative Classroom* in the How-To Handbook.

Assessing Understanding

As students experience the lessons in this module, they will achieve the module and lesson outcomes at different times. The more you know about students' current conceptions and understanding of the concepts the lessons present, the better able you will be to assess their conceptual development. For that reason, we recommend that you take time before beginning the module to conduct brief interviews with all students, or at least a random sample of the students, in your classroom. Although the interviews might be time-consuming, they will provide an important baseline from which you can assess the progress of students and the flow of the module.

We recommend ongoing assessment. Most tasks in which students are engaged lend themselves to assessment, either formal or informal. See the *Assessment Indicators* in the Outcomes chart and the *Assessment Strategies* in each lesson for specific suggestions.

Whenever you can, use BLM MO-1, *Notes for Assessing Understanding and Ability,* and actually document students' progress. *The Assessment Checklist,* BLM MO-2, provides a form for documenting students' achievement of the module outcomes. Used together, the two blackline masters, MO-1 and MO-2, will help you structure the assessment of students' progress throughout the module.

For further information about assessing student learning, see *How To Assess Student Understanding* in the How-To Handbook.

Notes for Assessing Understanding and Ability

Student's Name	Conceptual Understanding	Scientific Inquiry	Ability & Understanding	Collaborative Ability

Module Overview
Investigating Position and Motion

BLM MO-1

Assessment Checklist

Use this checklist to record your assessment of each student's understanding of the module outcomes. Duplicate as many copies as you need for your class.

NAME	Understands that an object's position can be described by locating it relative to other objects.	Understands that an object's motion can be described by tracing its position over time.	Understands that objects move in many different ways.	Understands that an object's motion can be described by measuring its position over time.	Shows basic skills for working in collaborative teams.	Asks for and gives help in his or her collaborative team.

Module Overview
Investigating Position and Motion

BLM MO-2

Module at a Glance

To complete the sequence of lessons in this module, you will need approximately 21 sessions of at least 25-30 minutes each, depending on the background of your students and on the time you allow for the discussion of students' experiences. The lessons require additional time for students to make observations, record data, and share their data and understanding with classmates. The order of the lessons in this module promotes conceptual development as students are allowed to construct their understanding over time. Therefore, you should teach the lessons sequentially. An instructional model, referred to as the "5Es"—engage, explore, explain, elaborate, and evaluate—structures the sequence of lessons. The following chart describes the organization of this module.

Lesson Title and Stage of Instructional Model	Purpose of Lesson	What Students Do
Introductory Lesson Doing Science 4 Sessions	To guide you and the students in preparing for inquiry-oriented, collaborative science experiences	Students are introduced to the processes of scientific inquiry, the skills of collaboration, and the characters C.Q. and I.O. Students set up their science folders in which they keep their record pages and other written data. The lesson also provides a structure for getting the classroom and students organized for activity-based science.
Lesson 1 I Spy **Engage** 1 Session	To assess how students currently describe the position of objects To engage students' interest in describing position	Students make cardboard binoculars and use them to play *I Spy* with their teams. After several rounds of the game, teams list words that were helpful in locating objects in the game and compile these into a class chart.
Lesson 2 Who Is Where? **Explore** 1 Session	To allow students to describe position in relation to themselves and to other students To introduce the idea of describing someone's position as "to the right/left of" someone else	The class reviews their chart of words that help describe the position of objects and considers adding **to the left/right of** to the list. Students share ideas for remembering which is left or right. They use the ideas as they play the *Who Is Where Game*.

Lesson Title and Stage of Instructional Model	Purpose of Lesson	What Students Do
Lesson 3 Where From C.Q.? **Explore** 2 Sessions	To create a need for students to describe the position of objects with greater accuracy To provide an opportunity for students to explore position as described in terms of two directions from an object	The class uses a stand-up figure of C.Q. and a yarn quadrant to describe students' positions in terms of two directions from C.Q. Then, each team places a crayon on the quadrant as directed by their Put-It-In-Position card. After all crayons are in position, teams describe the position of any six crayons. As a class, students compare the descriptions with the placement of the crayons.
Lesson 4 Where From What? **Explain** 2 Sessions	To allow students to express their understanding of describing position relative to another object To provide a useful term after students have expressed the idea in their own language	C.Q. and I.O. introduce an incomplete treasure map. Teams consider the problem of what they need to know to find the treasure. Once students express their ideas, the teacher introduces the term **reference object**. Then, teams play *I Spy* with a focus on the reference objects.
Lesson 5 More Than Direction **Elaborate** 1 Session or more	To establish a need for students to describe the position of an object with greater accuracy	Each team sets up its own yarn quadrant, hides a message under a specific cup, and writes directions to the cup. Teams trade quadrants and directions with other teams to play a game called *Find the Message.* Then, the *Find-the-Crab's-Name Page* challenges students to apply what they have learned.

Lesson Title and Stage of Instructional Model	Purpose of Lesson	What Students Do
Lesson 6 Where Is "Here"? **Elaborate** ⏰ 2 Sessions	To help students connect describing relative position to their daily lives To allow students to represent the positions of objects graphically	Students consider how people find and describe a position without C.Q. and the yarn sections. They think about everyday applications such as addresses and maps. Students help the teacher make a simple map of the classroom. Then teams draw their own basic maps of the playground and use the maps to play the *You Are Here Game*.
Lesson 7 Picture the Position **Elaborate/Evaluate** ⏰ 2 Sessions, plus additional time to interview individual students	To continue developing students' ability to describe position from a reference object other than themselves To allow students and the teacher to assess students' understanding of describing relative position	Teams look at a picture of the zany town of Norule. They locate specific objects in the picture and describe the position of the objects in relation to a variety of other objects. As teams work, each student demonstrates understanding of relative position in an individual interview with the teacher.
Lesson 8 Changing Position **Engage** ⏰ 1 Session	To assess students' current understanding of describing the motion of objects To engage students' interest in describing the motion of objects	Students reflect on the changing position of their sticky notes on team playground maps in Lesson 6. Then, they look at sets of *Before* and *After* pictures for evidence of motion, resulting in changes in position. Students develop a class chart of ways to describe motion. Then, students record their ideas in their science folders.

Lesson Title and Stage of Instructional Model	Purpose of Lesson	What Students Do
Lesson 9 Motion and Paths **Explore** 2 Sessions	To allow students to explore paths as a record of motion To allow students to graphically record motion	Students listen to a story about a Scwinch who makes many yarn paths from his house to the delicious scwizzle plants. On their record page, students trace imaginary paths that the Scwinch could have taken. Then, students create I.O.'s path on a ski map by matching pictures of I.O. skiing with the corresponding locations on the map.
Lesson 10 How Did It Move? **Explain/Elaborate** 4 Sessions or more	To allow students to describe a variety of motions To allow students to graphically record motion	Students consider that paths of moving objects usually are invisible. Then, teams do five investigations in which they observe and record the motion of a rubber ball. Afterward, each team makes a poster of one of the investigations and shares it with the class.
Lesson 11 Drop Races **Elaborate/Evaluate** 3 Sessions	To allow students to describe the speed of objects To assess students' understanding, in a new context, of how the motion of objects can be described	Teams race drops of liquid starch and water down a ramp and determine the faster and slower of the two drops. Then, teams create a mixture of starch and water from their own formula and race drops of the three liquids. Students consider time and distance as they compare the speed of each drop. Students show what they know about describing motion by changing the direction and speed of drops and describing the resulting changes in motion.

Advance Preparations

Before teaching the module, you will need to make the following special arrangements, purchases, and preparations.

The *Prepare Ahead* sections in the individual lessons will remind you of these preparations in advance.

Lesson 1

Introduce and thoroughly review with the students the *Doing Science* section of the student guide. Direct students to make their science folders so they will be ready for use in Lesson 1.

Each student will need two toilet paper tubes for Lesson1. In addition, you will need two for yourself. You could request that parents send in tubes with their children, post a notice in the workroom and staff bathrooms, and save tubes from your own household.

Guidelines for Using the Student Guide and Resource Book

You might question the use of a book for students in a hands-on science program. This book functions as a student guide and resource book, rather than as a traditional, read-about-science text. We designed the student guide to:

- help students to become more responsible for their own learning,
- enable students to manage the hands-on activities themselves rather than making it the sole responsibility of the teacher,
- provide an effective structure for collaborative learning,
- promote conceptual development and classroom management,
- develop a conceptual and logistical flow among the lessons in the module,
- motivate beginning readers and reinforce language arts skills in a meaningful way, and
- help students learn to follow directions and to make decisions about how to complete investigations.

Because reading levels differ widely within individual classes as well as throughout the country, *you* are the expert in deciding how you will use the student guide with your students. You might begin the year by reviewing all directions and text with the students before they proceed with their investigations. Then, gradually, you can turn over more and more of the responsibility to the students as they become more proficient readers. However, even readers with limited proficiency find it useful to know where to find information if they forget what to do. You can always turn students back to their guides if they cannot remember what to do next. This way, students can become more involved in their own learning process and can learn to rely on classmates and teammates, not just on you, for information, assistance, and guidance.

The student guide will help you to become a true facilitator of learning instead of serving as the sole "dispenser of knowledge and information."

Communication with Parents and Guardians

Within the blackline masters, you will find BLM MO-3, *Sample Letter to Parents and Guardians*. You may adapt it and duplicate it as you think appropriate, or use it as the basis for an article in your school's newsletter. Use it to enlist the support and help of parents and guardians. The more parents and guardians become involved in their child's learning, the more students will learn! Include local resources or events in the community that might enhance students' understanding of the ideas and skills presented in this module.

References

American Association for the Advancement of Science. 1993. *Benchmarks for Science Literacy.* New York: Oxford University Press.

Berger, C.F., et al. 1974. *Modular Activities Program in Science-Level 1* (teacher's annotated edition). Boston, MA: Houghton Mifflin Company.

Berger, C.F., et al. 1974. *Modular Activities Program in Science-Level 2* (teacher's annotated edition). Boston, MA: Houghton Mifflin Company.

Berger, C.F., et al. 1974. *Modular Activities Program in Science-Level 3* (teacher's annotated edition). Boston, MA: Houghton Mifflin Company.

Carson, R. 1987. *Sense of Wonder.* New York: Harper & Row.

Geller, L.G. 1985. "Conversations in Kindergarten." *Science and Children* (April): 30–32.

McCormack, A.J. 1988. Visual/Spatial Thinking: an Essential Element of Elementary School Science. *CESI Monograph and Occasional Paper-Series 3* (March).

National Research Council. 1996. *National Science Education Standards.* Washington, DC: National Academy Press.

SCIS. 1978. *Relative Position and Motion* (teacher's guide). Chicago, IL: Rand McNally and Company.

SCIS. 1968. *Relativity* (teacher's guide). Lexington, MA: D.C. Heath and Company.

____. 1979. "Early Childhood: Spatial Concepts." *Science and Children* (November/December): 36–37.

Master List of Supplies Investigating Position and Motion

* = Item to be supplied in science kit.
✓ = Item needed in lesson. Quantity may vary.

The following is a complete list of supplies needed for this module. Quantities are based on a class of 30 students.

Lesson Number	Intro	1	2	3	4	5	6	7	8	9	10	11
Supply Description												
Advertisement								✓				
*Balls, small, rubber											10	
Binoculars (optional)		✓										
Blackboard							✓		✓			
BLM MO-1, *Notes for Assessing Understanding and Ability*		✓	✓	✓	✓	✓	✓	✓	✓	✓	✓	✓
BLM MO-2, *Assessment Checklist*					✓			✓			✓	✓
BLM MO-3, *Sample Letter to Parents and Guardians*		✓										
BLM 3-1, *Put-It-In-Position Cards*				✓								
BLM 3-2, *Put-It-In Position Record Page*				10								
BLM 5-1, *Find-the-Crab's-Name Page*						10						
BLM 5-2, *How to Find the Crab's Name Page*						10						
BLM 7-1, *Picture the Position Record Page*								30				
BLM 9-1, *The Scwinch's Paths*										30		
BLM 9-2, *I.O.'s Path Record Page*										30		
BLM 10-1, *Describing Motion Record Page*											10	
BLM 11-1, *Drop Races Record Page*												10
*Bottle (dropper)												30
*Bowls, round, plastic, (approximately 15 x 30 cm)												5

Master List of Supplies

Lesson Number	Intro	1	2	3	4	5	6	7	8	9	10	11
Supply Description												
Box Lids, shallow (copier paper box lids)											5	
Cassette of music			✓									
Chalk						✓		✓				
Crayons, assorted colors				10	1							
Crayons, blue										30		
Crayons, pink										30		
Crayons, any two other colors										60		
*Cup, measuring (500ml)												1
*Cup, 4 oz. paper						120						
*C.Q. Stand-Up Figure		✓	✓	✓	✓	✓	✓	✓	✓	✓	✓	✓
Envelope, small							1					
*Food Coloring, blue												1
Folder, two-pocket	30	✓	✓	✓	✓	✓	✓	✓	✓	✓	✓	✓
*Food Coloring, yellow												1
*Funnel												1
Map (simple as possible)							✓					
Map (showing school's fire escape route)							✓					
Markers, non-toxic	✓	✓		✓	✓	✓	✓	✓	✓		✓	
Marker, non-toxic, black			1									
Miscellaneous Items (eye glasses, a whistle, or a pencil)		✓										
Miscellaneous Items (whistle, bell or other noise-making device)							✓					
Paper, chart		✓		✓	✓	✓	✓	✓	✓		✓	
Paper clips, #3-small (1 box)							✓					
Paper, construction 9 x 12			✓				10					
Paper, construction, 12 x 18 (one red, one yellow, and two other light colors)			✓	4								
Paper, construction, 12 x18 (light color)										10+		

Lesson Number / Supply Description	Intro	1	2	3	4	5	6	7	8	9	10	11
Paper, drawing	✓					✓	✓				✓	
Paper towels (roll)												✓
Paper, writing	✓	✓		✓	✓						✓	
Pencil w/eraser		✓		✓	✓	✓	✓	✓	✓	✓	✓	✓
*Raceboard											10	
*Rubber Bands, red (medium width)						10						
*Rubber Bands, yellow (medium width)						10						
Science Folder		✓			✓	✓			✓			
Scissors			✓	✓		✓					✓	
*Starch, liquid, laundry (container)											1	
Sticky-pad, 1½ x 2							✓					
Sticky-pad, 3 x 3							✓					
*String, 30 cm lengths											10	
Tape, masking	✓		✓		✓	✓			✓			
*Tape measurer (metric)											10	
Tape Player			✓									
Toilet Paper tubes		60										
Tote Bag							✓					
*Tray							✓					10
Water												✓
Where's Waldo Book, or comic strip (optional)							✓					
*Wristbands	30	✓	✓	✓	✓	✓	✓	✓	✓	✓	✓	✓
Writing board (such as a clipboard, tray or book)									30			
*Yarn, blue (1 skein)			✓	✓	✓							
*Yarn, green (1 skein)			✓	✓	✓							

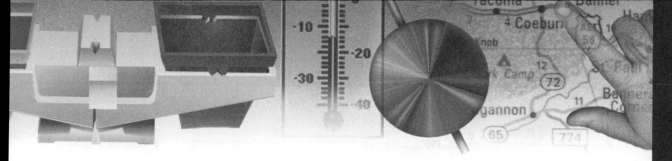

Doing Science

This lesson engages students in thinking about science by introducing them to the processes of scientific inquiry. The lesson also introduces the skills of collaboration and the characters, C.Q. and I.O., who help students with inquiry and concept development. During this lesson, students also set up their science folders in which they keep their record pages and all other written data throughout the module. The lesson also provides a structure for getting your classroom and students organized for activity-based science.

Estimated Time:
4 class sessions

Note: The *Doing Science* lesson is the same in each of the science modules at a grade level. The students need to experience this lesson only once. Therefore, if students have already completed one science module of *BSCS Science T.R.A.C.S.*, they do not need to go through this lesson in detail. We recommend that you review the information with the students as necessary before they begin a new module. Note that the technology module begins with *Doing Technology*, which introduces students to the processes of technological design. The lesson includes the same information about teamwork, C.Q. and I.O., and making and using science folders or journals, however. Review this information as needed.

Purpose: To guide you and the students in preparing for inquiry-oriented, collaborative science experiences

OUTCOMES	ASSESSMENT INDICATORS
	Students show they have achieved the outcome by:
Conceptual	
Students become engaged in the enterprise of science.	• expressing their ideas about science and scientists, • discussing the basic skills of scientific inquiry, and • making their science folders.
Scientific Inquiry	
Understandings Students become aware of the inquiry processes scientists use in their work.	• reading about, discussing, and describing the basic skills of scientific inquiry.
Collaborative	
Students become engaged in teamwork.	• describing and demonstrating the basic collaborative skills used in this program.

Supplies

(**Note:** The supplies listed are those we recommend for students' science folders. If you usually use another method of record keeping, such as a journal or another type of folder, then substitute the materials you usually use for those in this list.)

For Each Student:
- 1 two-pocket folder
- 6 sheets of writing paper
- 6 sheets of drawing paper
- markers, non-toxic or crayons

Before You Begin

▶ Review the student pages for this lesson.

▶ Review the *Information for the Teacher* at the end of this lesson.

▶ If you have not already done so, review the *Program Overview* and the following sections from the *How-To Handbook:*

- *How To Manage the Classroom for Hands-on Science and Technology*
- *How To Involve Students in Scientific Inquiry and Technological Design*
- *How To Create a Collaborative Classroom*
- *How To Use Journals to Promote Understanding*

▶ Locate the colored, stretchy wristbands in the kit of materials. Choose a color of wristband to correspond with each team job. Make a poster that displays which color represents which job. Display the poster when you introduce the team jobs.

▶ Decide on the type of folder or journal you would like the students to use for organizing their record pages during this module. Gather the necessary materials.

▶ Post the *Team Skills* and *Team Jobs* posters in a prominent place. Leave the posters on display throughout the year.

▶ Set aside space on a bulletin board to display students' drawings of scientists.

Teaching Strategies   Session 1

★ See student page 1

1. Exploring Students' Ideas About Science

▶ Find out students' current conceptions of science and scientists by asking them to answer the questions on the opening page.

- Before holding a class discussion, allow students to draw pictures independently.

- Ask students to share their drawings and then post them on a bulletin board so that students can compare their ideas.

▶ As students present their drawings of scientists, you might tally responses about the following:

- number of males and females,
- number of racial or ethnic groups represented,
- instruments,
- symbols,
- clothing,
- setting, and
- other significant events or objects.

From studies done with children, researchers have found that the stereotype of a scientist is a white male wearing a lab coat and working with a lot of test tubes and chemicals in a laboratory. Often children depict scientists as balding, wearing glasses, and with peculiar facial features that indicate some type of bizarre behavior. We encourage you to dispel such myths and stereotypes by introducing students to real scientists from books, films, the Internet, or from your local community as students complete the lessons in this module.

INTRODUCTION
Doing Science

What Is Science?

science...

scientist...

Read these questions. Draw pictures to show what you think.
1. What do people do when they do science?
2. What is a scientist like?
3. Can you be a scientist right now?
4. What would you be doing if you were doing science?

Doing Science 1

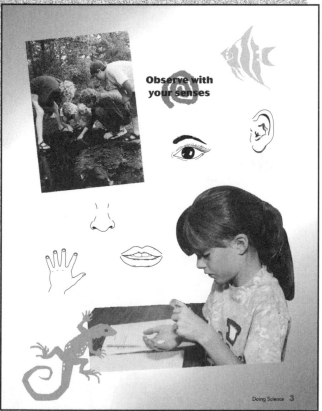

▶ Find out if any of the students' family members are scientists and invite those family members or scientists in the community to visit the class and talk about their work.

If possible, invite female scientists and those from diverse ethnic backgrounds.

▶ Repeat this activity at the conclusion of the module to find out whether students' ideas about science and scientists have changed.

★ See student pages 2–8

Teaching Strategies   Session 2

2. Engaging Students in Inquiry-based Science

▶ Review the phrases and photographs under the heading *How Can You Do Science?*

- Point out to students that the photographs show students and scientists doing similar things.
- Invite students to describe briefly what they think the scientists and students are doing at each step.

Keep this discussion brief. The purpose of this lesson is to make students aware that they do many of the same kinds of things that scientists do. Students will experience all aspects of scientific inquiry and will reflect on their experiences throughout the module.

Wonder. Ask students what they think scientists might wonder about.

If you have not done so, review the Information for the Teacher *and* How To Involve Students in Scientific Inquiry and Technological Design. *The description of science in those sections indicates that scientists wonder about objects, organisms, or events; they investigate to find out more; and then their new findings raise new questions that cause them to wonder again.*

Doing Science   **27**

Ask questions. Find out what questions about the world around them students would like to answer. Help them distinguish between questions that they can answer by investigating, such as "How does a guppy move?" versus questions that they can answer only by reading or talking with an expert, such as "Why is the sky blue?" or "How do mountains form?"

Both types of questions are legitimate, but the lessons emphasize questions that students can answer by investigating.

Observe with your senses. Invite them to demonstrate observing with all of their senses. When might they use their sense of sight, hearing, smell, touch, or taste?

*Reinforce that scientists **do not** use their sense of taste, except when they know what they are tasting. Students will not taste anything in science class. The lessons reinforce this safety issue with the students.*

Investigate. Ask students what they would do to find out about something they know nothing about. What might they look for? What might they do?

If students mention "doing experiments," ask them to describe how they would do an experiment in science.

As students progress through this program, they will learn about such investigations as "fair tests" in which they must control variables. In the primary years, students' investigations will emphasize making systematic observations, describing and recording what they observe, and drawing conclusions from their observations.

Use tools. Ask what tools students think scientists use.

They probably will mention such familiar tools as microscopes, telescopes,

Investigate

4 Introduction

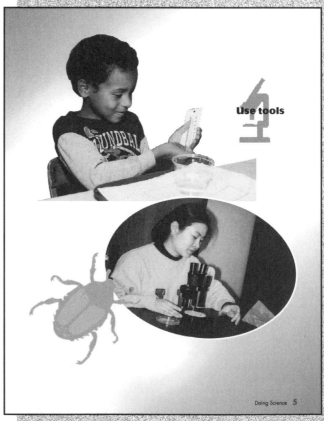

Use tools

Doing Science 5

computers, and test tubes. They might realize that familiar objects such as rulers, thermometers, and cups can be tools for scientists, too. See the suggestion at the end of this section about unpacking the kit of materials with students so they become familiar with the tools they will use in science class.

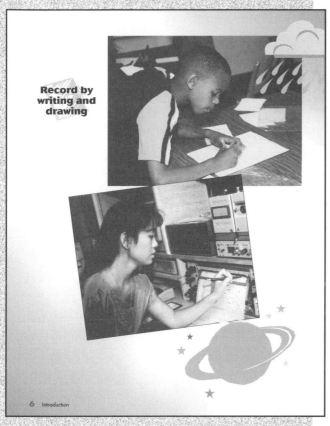

Record by writing and drawing. Discuss recording information and keeping records.

- Who keeps records?
- Why do people keep records?
- Where might they keep records?

Mention that students will keep a special science folder for their records. They will make their science folders in Session 4.

Share your ideas. Discuss the importance of sharing ideas with one another and communicating information and ideas.

Doing Science **29**

Students will discuss this further in the section about collaborative work.

Wonder and ask new questions. Ask students why they think "wonder" begins and ends this list. Explain that when scientists get new information about something, this new information often raises new questions. Scientists are people who always are wondering why and "what would happen if . . ."

If you have not done so already, unpack the kit of materials with students. Show them the items that come in the kit and ask them to speculate what each item might be for.

This can be a very motivating way to introduce students to the module and to some simple tools of science. They can anticipate using the equipment and materials in the upcoming lessons.

★ See student pages 9–13

Teaching Strategies   Session 3

3. Introducing Collaborative Learning

▶ Ask students if they think scientists usually work together or alone and to explain why they think so.

  • Ask them to consider the advantages and disadvantages of working alone or with other people.

  • Review the photographs of scientists in the previous section that show scientists working with others.

▶ Focus students' attention on working in a team.

  • Ask them to describe a time they have worked with others to accomplish something.

  • Explain that they will work in teams of three in science.

Working Together to Do Science

Team Skills
Move into your teams quickly and quietly.

Stay with your teams.

Doing Science 9

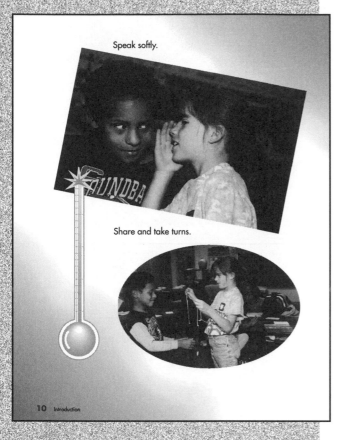

Speak softly.

Share and take turns.

10 Introduction

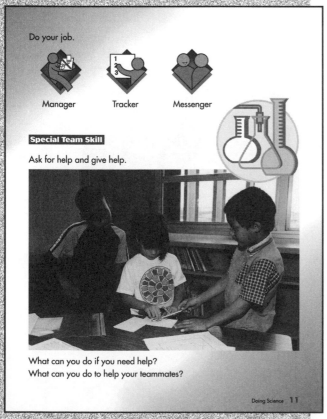

Do your job.

Manager   Tracker   Messenger

Special Team Skill

Ask for help and give help.

What can you do if you need help?
What can you do to help your teammates?

Doing Science 11

• Tell students that you will assign the teams and that students will work with different teammates during this module.

Remind students that they will not always work with their friends and that one purpose of collaborative learning is to learn to work with many different people.

• Ask students to describe what you should see and hear when they work in a team.

• If necessary, describe your expectations about respecting and being polite to their teammates.

▶ Explain that working well in a team takes special skills. Introduce the team skills, one at a time.

• Invite students to explain and demonstrate each skill.

For example, moving into teams quickly and quietly does not mean running to their workstations. Speaking softly means talking so only their partner can hear them. Sharing and taking turns means sharing and taking turns in two ways: (1) sharing the supplies, and (2) sharing their ideas with their partner.

• Tell students that they will practice these skills every time they work with their partners.

• Point out the *Team Skills* posters that will remind them of these skills.

▶ Introduce the "special team skill."

• Tell them that the skill, ask for help and give help, is a special one that they will work on this year.

• Ask them to describe and demonstrate how they might ask for help if they get stuck or need something.

• Ask them to describe and demonstrate how they might offer help to a teammate.

Doing Science **31**

You can use these techniques throughout the module to help reinforce the collaborative skills that students are developing. Learning to work with others takes time and students need to reflect often on their collaborative work to improve their skills.

▶ Introduce the team jobs.

- Explain that you will assign the jobs, but that they will have a chance to do all three jobs.
- Point out and explain the use of the supply table for the managers.

You might have students turn to the list of supplies in Lesson 1 and show the students that the manager gets and returns the supplies shown in that list.

- Explain that the tracker makes sure that the team follows the steps in the directions when they are engaged in a team activity.

You might ask students to turn to the set of directions in Lesson 1 and point out the numbered steps. Remind students that the tracker does not have to be the only "reader"; the tracker simply keeps track of which step the team is completing.

- Review the messenger's job.
- Remind students that the messenger is not the reporter for the team.

If necessary, review the description of the messenger's job in How To Create a Collaborative Classroom *in the How-To Handbook.*

- Show students the colored wristbands and the poster that displays which color of wristband corresponds to each job. Explain that whenever they work in teams, each teammate will wear a wristband that shows which job he or she is performing.
- Point out the *Team Jobs* posters that review the responsibilities of each job.

Team Jobs

The manager gets the supplies and returns them.

The tracker makes sure that the team follows the directions in order.

12　Introduction

The messenger may ask another messenger for help.

The messenger may ask the teacher for help.

Doing Science　13

Teaching Strategies   Session 4

★ See student pages 14–17

4. Introducing the Characters, C.Q. and I.O.

▶ Read with students *Doing Science With C.Q. and I.O.* on page 14.

- Ask them what C.Q.'s and I.O.'s names stand for.
- Ask students what it means to be **curious**.
- Review their understanding of the terms **investigate** and **observe**.

▶ Tell students that they will encounter C.Q. and I.O. throughout their student guides. Invite them to find examples of C.Q. and I.O. in their guides.

5. Making Science Folders

Note: We recommend that primary students use a two-pocket folder to keep their record pages and other drawings and notes organized during the lessons in this module. Feel free to use another method of record keeping if students are familiar with journals or use other types of folders in other subject areas.

▶ Read and discuss with students the opening illustrations in this section.

▶ Distribute a two-pocket folder to each student and instruct students to make their folders by doing the following things.

- Put their names on their folders.
- Decorate the cover of their folders.
- Place the writing and drawing paper inside their folders.

Alternatively, distribute the materials appropriate for your method of record keeping and instruct students accordingly.

▶ Spend some time talking about the purpose of the science folders and when you would like them to use their folders.

- Point out the icons of the record page and science folder on page 16 that will remind students when they are to record something.
- Encourage independent use of the folders.

Students should feel comfortable writing and drawing in their folders whenever they have something they want to record. See How To Use Journals to Promote Understanding *in the How-To Handbook for more information about how students might make use of their science folders.*

- Explain where you would like them to store their folders.

6. Previewing the Student Guide

▶ Take time to walk students through their student guides.

- Point out the characters, C.Q. and I.O.
- Point out the Team Task, Team Skill, Team Jobs, Team Supplies, and Directions so that students know when they will be working in teams.
- Ask students to describe how they think this guide will help them work like scientists do.

7. Closing the Lesson

▶ Review page 17 with the students.

- Ask students why they think this page shows an invitation.
- Tell them that this invitation invites them to be curious and "do science" throughout this module.

Information for the Teacher

About Doing Science

> Students should be actively involved in exploring phenomena that interest them both in and out of class. These investigations should be fun and exciting, opening the door to even more things to explore. An important part of students' exploration is telling others what they see, what they think, and what it makes them wonder about. Children should have lots of time to talk about what they observe and to compare their observations with those of others. A premium should be placed on careful expression, a necessity in science, but students at this level should not be expected to come up with scientifically accurate explanations for their observations. Theory can wait.
>
> —AAAS, *Benchmarks for Science Literacy,* p. 10

The primary goal of this lesson, and of the entire curriculum, is to involve children in the doing of science—to allow them to explore the world around them and to describe what they observe. Thus, the title of this introductory lesson: *Doing Science.* This lesson is designed to engage students in three important aspects of doing science in this program:

- scientific inquiry,
- collaborative work, and
- the systematic recording of data in a journal or science folder.

The following sections provide additional background information as you begin your adventures with students in doing science. @

The Nature of Science and Scientific Inquiry

First and foremost, we believe that everyone, children and adults alike, *can* do science. Science is not just for those with specialized knowledge, but is for anyone who is curious and has questions about how the world works. @

What Science Is

Scientists share certain basic beliefs and attitudes about what they do and how they view their work. These are the attitudes and beliefs that we would like to instill in students as they explore the world around them.

- The world is understandable.
- Scientific ideas are subject to change.
- Scientific knowledge is durable.
- Science cannot provide complete answers to all questions.
- Science demands evidence.
- Science is a blend of logic and imagination.
- Science explains and predicts.
- Scientists try to identify and avoid bias.
- Science is not authoritarian.
- Science is a complex social activity.
- Science is organized into content disciplines and is conducted in various institutions.
- There are generally accepted ethical principles in the conduct of science.
- Scientists participate in public affairs both as specialists and as citizens.

—AAAS, *Science for All Americans,* pp. 25-30

What Scientific Inquiry Is

The enterprise of science encourages wonder, creativity, curiosity, questioning, skepticism, perseverance, cooperation, and collaboration. Scientists do not use one scientific method in their work. They observe, measure, record their observations, talk to others in their field, write about their findings, read about others' findings, refine their questions, gather and analyze additional data, make predictions, and ask more questions.

All of these skills and attitudes are developed through the processes of scientific inquiry, as stated in the *National Science Education Standards* and *Benchmarks for Science Literacy*.

Probably the most important factor in doing science is to let children be children.

- Allow freedom and flexibility as students explore objects, events, and organisms.

- Let them come up with questions of interest to them and give them a lot of time to talk about what they see and do.

- Help them structure their data-gathering activities and encourage them to build explanations from their observations and data.

- Constantly ask them what they think and why they think so.

- Do not expect that students of this age will come up with scientifically accurate explanations as a scientist might explain the same events. However, help students work toward scientific understanding by encouraging them to base their explanations on reasoned thinking that results from their experiences, data, readings, and dialogue with their classmates.

See *How To Involve Students in Scientific Inquiry and Technological Design* in the How-To Handbook for a more complete description of the processes of scientific inquiry. @

The Importance of Collaborative Work in Science

One of the important structural aspects of this curriculum is its built-in collaborative design, indicated whenever students see Team Task, Team Skill, Team Jobs, Team Supplies, and Directions for a collaborative activity. Often, people see the primary purpose of collaborative learning as the development of students' social skills—improving their ability to work effectively with others. Although social skills are important, we believe that the *primary* goal of collaborative work is to promote learning and conceptual development. Because most knowledge is constructed socially, we encourage students to work with others with whom they can share their thinking, but who might challenge their points of view, offer different perspectives, and extend their ideas.

Although each student must construct her or his own understanding of phenomena, interaction with peers can add significantly to a student's depth of understanding and knowledge base. In these interactions, students both give and receive ideas. They clarify their own thinking, both orally and in writing, and they consider the viewpoints of their classmates.

We encourage you to structure such a collaborative atmosphere within the classroom, one in which students can explore phenomena, collect and organize data, share their ideas, develop convincing arguments for their points of view, and enter into meaningful dialogue with their science "colleagues." Because most students are not used to working together in a collaborative way, expect this to take some time. The students need time to develop their skills in working together. Collaboration will not happen overnight!

We recognize that true collaboration is not an easy task because it includes managing materials, managing experiences, and managing discourse. It demands new skills on the parts of the teacher and of the students. That is why we have built in as much structure as possible and suggested strategies throughout the lessons to help you and the students work collaboratively. See *How To Create a Collaborative Classroom* in the How-To Handbook for more help in structuring your classroom for collaboration. @

Keeping Science Folders or Journals in the Classroom

Science folders in the primary grades and science journals in the upper grades are essential for doing science. Without written records, it is difficult for students to remember what they have done, what happened in an investigation, or how their thinking is changing. Providing students an opportunity to write or draw gives them the time they need to reflect on their experiences and process their thoughts. Initially, students labor over their writing, but, as time goes by, even reluctant writers become better able to express themselves. Writing helps students clarify their thinking and develop reasoned explanations from their experiences. The results are worth the effort!

See *How To Use Journals to Promote Understanding* in the How-To Handbook for suggestions about how to make science folders and journals a regular feature of students' science experiences. @

I Spy

Students each make a pair of binoculars from cardboard tubes, and use them to play *I Spy* with their teams. After several rounds of the game, teams list words that were helpful in locating objects in the game and compile these into a class chart.

Purpose: To assess students' current understanding of describing the position of objects

To engage students' interest in describing position

OUTCOMES	ASSESSMENT INDICATORS
	Students show they have achieved the outcome by:
Conceptual	
Students express their current understanding of describing the position of objects.	• describing the location of an object so that others can guess the identity of the object, • identifying a specific object from another's description of the object's location, and • deciding which words were helpful in describing location.
Scientific Inquiry	
Understandings Students become aware that they can use simple tools to extend the senses.	• talking about when they might need to use real binoculars during a game of *I Spy*.
Collaborative	
Students use basic skills for working in a team.	• staying with their teammates as they play *I Spy* and as they make their lists, • speaking softly to their teammates, and • taking turns spying and guessing.

Supplies

For the Entire Class:
- an item for the teacher such as glasses, a whistle, or a pencil
- chart paper
- markers, non-toxic
- masking tape
- a supply of writing paper
- binoculars (optional)

For Each Student:
- 2 toilet paper tubes
- masking tape
- marker, non-toxic
- science folder
- pencil

Before You Begin

▶ If you have not already done so, introduce and thoroughly review with the students the *Doing Science* lesson of the student guide. Direct students to make their science folders so they will be ready for Lesson 1.

▶ Review the pages in the student guide for this lesson. Using the directions, make your own set of "binoculars."

▶ Decide which students you will assign to each team of three for this module. The students will remain in these teams at least through Lesson 7. Be sure each team consists of both boys and girls, as well as students with differing levels of ability. Make a record of these assignments. (See *How To Create a Collaborative Classroom* in the How-To Handbook.)

▶ Organize the classroom for hands-on science and collaboration by planning four different areas.
  • Provide a workstation for each team of three.
  • Clear a group area—floor space for the entire class to sit with you.
  • Set up a supply area where team managers will pick up and return supplies.
  • Organize a storage area for science folders and team projects.

  (See *How To Manage the Classroom for Hands-on Science and Technology* in the How-To Handbook.)

▶ Duplicate enough copies of BLM MO-1, *Notes for Assessing Understanding and Ability,* so that you can keep written records of responses, comments, and significant events that will help you track each student's conceptual development. (See *How To Assess Student Understanding* in the How-To Handbook.)

▶ Place the toilet paper tubes, a quantity of masking tape, and markers on the supply table.

Teaching Strategies   Session 1

★ See student pages 19–20

1. Introducing the Lesson

▶ Assemble the class in the large group area.

▶ Pretend to have misplaced some item. For example, while wearing your glasses on top of your head, pretend to be looking for them.

- Request students' help in finding the "lost" item.
- Find the "lost" item from the students' description.

▶ Using the incident as a lead-in, read and discuss the student guide through the activity, *Making Binoculars*.

2. Making Binoculars—Individual Task

▶ Review the task as necessary. Point out the markers and tape, and have students make their binoculars.

▶ Although this is an individual task, encourage students to help one another in taping the binoculars and making sure the ends of the tubes are even.

★ See student pages 21–23

3. Playing *I Spy*—Team Task

▶ After students finish their binoculars, assemble the class in the group area to introduce *I Spy*. Direct students to place their binoculars in their laps temporarily.

- Using your own set of cardboard binoculars, model the game by looking through them and by "spying" an object.
- Describe the location of the object, and invite students to use their binoculars to "spy" the object.

Begin by giving one or two descriptors of the location of the object. "It is in front of my desk near the trash can." If students cannot guess the object, add other phrases to describe the location.

LESSON 1

I Spy

Finding the soccer ball is really important when you want to play soccer! Describe where the ball is so that the children would be able to find it.

How well can you describe where something is? In the game, I Spy, someone describes **where** an object is, and others guess **what** the object is. You will play I Spy. But first make something to use in the game.

ENGAGE **19**

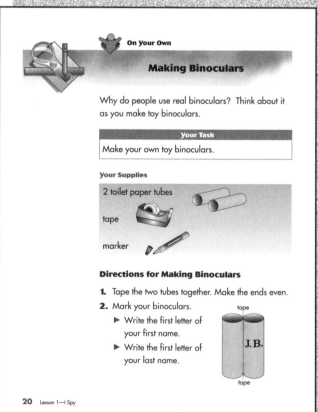

On Your Own

Making Binoculars

Why do people use real binoculars? Think about it as you make toy binoculars.

Your Task
Make your own toy binoculars.

Your Supplies

2 toilet paper tubes

tape

marker

Directions for Making Binoculars

1. Tape the two tubes together. Make the ends even.
2. Mark your binoculars.
   ▶ Write the first letter of your first name.
   ▶ Write the first letter of your last name.

tape

J.B.

tape

20   Lesson 1—I Spy

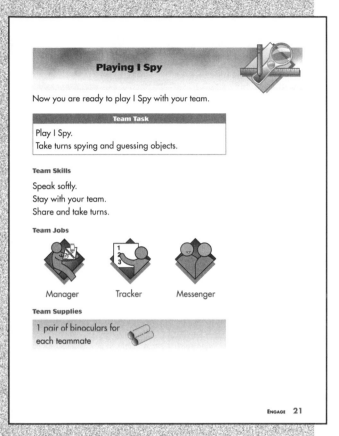

Playing I Spy

Now you are ready to play I Spy with your team.

Team Task

Play I Spy.
Take turns spying and guessing objects.

Team Skills

Speak softly.
Stay with your team.
Share and take turns.

Team Jobs

Manager   Tracker   Messenger

Team Supplies

1 pair of binoculars for
each teammate

ENGAGE **21**

- Play the game two or three times until the students have the idea.

▶ Together with the students, review the directions in their guide for playing *I Spy*. Invite the students to describe what the two team skills might look and sound like in the context of the game.

▶ Assign teams and workstations, and have teams begin the game.

▶ As teams play the game, listen and make note of how students describe the location of objects.

4. Listing Helpful Words—Team Task

▶ After teams play several rounds of the game, direct teams to complete *Checking Understanding*.

▶ Circulate among teams as they make their lists. Students might have difficulty remembering how they described where the objects were located.

▶ Encourage them to recall the objects, and then to recall how they described where the objects were.

Directions for Playing I Spy

1. Decide who will spy the first object. The spy-er will do these things.

- ▶ Look through your binoculars and choose one object.
- ▶ Don't tell your teammates what object you pick.
- ▶ Describe **where** the object is. C.Q. will show you how.

Now it is my turn. I spy an object on the floor between the door and the table.

Is it the trash can?

If your team is speaking softly, what will another team hear?

- ▶ If your teammates don't guess the right object, give them some more hints about **where** it is.
- ▶ If they still don't guess, tell them the object.

2. Take turns spying and guessing.

22   Lesson 1—I Spy

Checking Understanding

Do these things with your team.

1. Decide if you ever would need real binoculars to play I Spy. Tell when and why.

2. Think about the objects your team chose in I Spy. How did you describe where the objects were? Talk about it.

3. Some words help us describe where objects are. Write the words that helped you guess where the objects were.

4. Be ready to share your list with the class.

ENGAGE **23**

Assessment Strategies

★ See student page 24

At this point in the lesson, you have received an indication of how individual students currently describe the position of objects.

- You have observed students describe the position of objects, and guess other objects, based upon a description of position during the game of *I Spy*.

- You have listened and talked with students as teams listed helpful words and phrases in *Checking Understanding*.

5. Continuing Assessment

▶ Assemble teams with their lists in the group area.

- • Determine students' familiarity with tools that extend the senses by addressing the first question in *Checking Understanding*.

- • Invite students to discuss briefly the circumstances under which they might use real binoculars to play *I Spy*.

▶ Use information from your earlier observations to help students develop and discuss the class chart.

- • Ask teams to share words from their lists that are helpful in describing where an object is located.

- • Record students' responses on a class chart.

Record words and phrases just as students express them. Students might describe direction, distance, and location in position words rather than in relative terms. For example, they might suggest back, front, behind, near, and so forth, rather than to the right or left of . . . , in front of or behind . . . , between the . . . and the . . . , near to or far from the . . . Do not point out the difference at this time. However, list reference objects whenever students mention them.

Now, do these things on your own.
  Think of a time when you had to describe where something was.
  ▶ Write about it.
  ▶ Draw a picture of it.

▶ Ask students to think of a time they had to describe where something was.

- • Direct students to write and draw about such a time in their folders.

- • Review students' folders to gain further insight into students' thinking.

Who Is Where?

EXPLORE

Estimated Time:
1 class session

The class reviews their chart of words that help describe the position of objects, and consider adding **to the left/right of** to the list. Students share ideas for remembering which is left or right. They use the ideas as they play two parts of the *Who Is Where Game,* in which students name classmates whose positions match simple descriptions of position.

Purpose: To allow students to describe position in relation to themselves and to other students

To introduce the idea of describing someone's position as "to the right/left of" someone else

OUTCOMES	ASSESSMENT INDICATORS
	Students show they have achieved the outcome by:
Conceptual	
Students recognize that they describe the position of objects in relation to other objects.	<ul><li>stating who is **in front/back**, or **to the left/right** of *themselves* at intervals during a game, and</li><li>stating who is **in front/back**, or **to the left/right** of *someone else* at intervals during another game.</li></ul>
Students become aware that they describe the position of objects in terms of direction.	<ul><li>using directions such as **to the right/left** of and **in front/back of** to play a game, and</li><li>selecting objects by the description **in front of you** and **to the left of you** and drawing the objects in their science folders.</li></ul>

Supplies

For the Entire Class:
- 1 sheet each of red, yellow, blue, and orange construction paper, 9 inches x 12 inches
- black marker, non-toxic
- scissors
- tape player
- cassette of music
- class chart of helpful words from Lesson 1

Before You Begin

▶ Review the student pages for this lesson.

▶ Review the following sections of *Information for the Teacher.*
- *Expectations for Students' Use of Left/Right*
- *Strategies for Helping Students Remember Left from Right*
- *Directions for the Who Is Where Game*
- *Developing Visual/Spatial Thinking Abilities*

▶ Prepare placards for the game.
- Cut each sheet of construction paper into halves, 4-½" x 12".
- Print "to the right of" on both red sheets.
- Print "to the left of" on both yellow sheets.
- Print "in front of" on both orange sheets.
- Print "in back of" on both blue sheets.

▶ Review the game and decide where the class will play it.

Teaching Strategies   Session 1

★ See student pages 25–26

1. Introducing the Lesson

▶ Review the class chart of words that help describe the location or position of objects.

▶ In the student guide, read and discuss pages 25-26.

   • Encourage students to share with the class their techniques for remembering left/right.

   • If no one mentions the techniques listed in *Information for the Teacher*, share with the class these and any additional techniques.

2. Playing the *Who Is Where Game*

▶ Draw students' attention to the announcement about the game in the student guide.

▶ Introduce and play Part 1 of the *Who Is Where Game.* After students have mastered Part 1, go on to Part 2.

▶ During Part 2 of the game, if students have difficulty describing position from another's viewpoint, provide necessary support with the following strategies.

   • Introduce the idea of seeing with your "mind's eye". Explain the phrase as imagining you are in that person's position so you can describe position as that person sees it.

   • Encourage students temporarily to assume the position of the student holding the placard.

▶ Observe students as they play to gain insight into their ability to respond to direction in describing position. Take notes about individual students.

Who Is Where?

LESSON 2

"Which way to the swings, I.O.?"

"To the left, C.Q."

"Uh–oh! I forgot that C.Q. has trouble remembering left and right!"

EXPLORE   25

In the last lesson, you listed words that help you describe where something is. **Position** is a word that means "where something is." An object's position is where the object is; position describes the place of an object. "Left" and "right" can help you describe the place or position of an object. But, remembering which is left and which is right can be confusing.

"I never knew I had this freckle before. Great! Now I will always know that my right hand is the hand with the freckle."

Some people are lucky. Do you have any tricks to help you remember which is left and which is right? Share your tricks with the class.

The Who Is Where Game

Now you are ready to play the Who Is Where Game. This game lets you describe where you are and describe where your classmates are, too.

26   Lesson 2—Who Is Where?

3. Adding to the Class Chart

▶ After both parts of the game, invite students to add to the class chart words that help describe position— where people or objects are located.

- Students will likely suggest adding **front/back** and **left/right** to the chart. Add the words as suggested.

- Draw attention to the complete phrases on the placards. For example, *to the right of,* rather than just the descriptor *right.*

- Add each of the phrases to the class chart.

Because students are merely exploring their ideas about relative position, don't provide explanations about adding both the words and the phrases. Students will reflect on their common experiences from Lessons 1, 2, and 3 as they develop an explanation in Lesson 4.

Checking Understanding

Do these things in your science folder.

1. From your seat in the classroom, draw these things.
   ▶ Draw 2 objects you can see in front of you.
   ▶ Draw 2 objects you can see to the left of you.
2. Write "in front of me" on one picture.
3. Write "to the left of me" on the other picture.
4. Draw or tell C.Q. something to help him remember which way is left and which is right.

Assessment Strategies

Lesson 2 has enabled you to assess students' developing understanding of describing position.

- You have observed students' responses in describing their own position and the positions of others as they played the *Who Is Where Game.*
- You have noted the suggestions of individual students as you added words and phrases to the class chart.

★ See student page 27

4. Continuing Assessment— Individual Task

▶ The following task in *Checking Understanding* will provide you with additional information to use when assessing students' developing understanding of describing position relative to other objects.

▶ Introduce *Checking Understanding* in the student guide and explain that students are to draw in their own folders. Point out that "objects" may include other students.

▶ As students draw, circulate among them. Observe students' drawings, ask questions, and take notes to help you accurately interpret their drawings.

▶ When students complete the task, collect and review their folders. Interview students individually as necessary.

Information for the Teacher

Expectations for Students' Use of Left/Right

There is no expectation of mastery of accurate use of left/right for students in this module. Children (and adults) vary widely in this respect. Although this module provides opportunities for students to distinguish and to describe left/right, the primary intent is to help students construct their understanding of relative position. Provide any support necessary so that an inability to remember left from right does not hinder students' progress. @

Strategies for Helping Students Remember Left from Right

▶ Have students hold their hands out in front of them, palms out and fingers up. Point out that the forefinger and thumb of the left hand is the same shape as an upper case L.

▶ Mark the back of students' hands with nontoxic, washable markers—red, for right, and lemon yellow or lime green for left. @

Directions for the *Who Is Where Game*

▶ Play the game in a relatively open area.

▶ Assemble students in the area and randomly distribute the placards that read "to the right of," etc.

▶ As you play a tape of lively music, direct students to march randomly or move around the room, not in line or in any order. Students may move in any direction.

▶ As students move, ask them to pass the placards continually from one to another as they meet.

▶ When the music stops, have students hold the placards as follows:
  • To the left/right—Hold placard to the appropriate side.
  • In front of - Hold placard upright above head and forward.
  • In back of - Hold placard upright above head and slightly to the back.

Part 1: Students describe the position of others relative to themselves.

▶ One at a time, ask students holding placards to quickly respond to their placard by naming someone in front/back or to the left/right of them. (Robin says, "Tomas is to my right"or "Tomas is to the right of me.")

▶ When the music begins again, students continue to move and pass the placards until the music stops.

Part 2: Students describe the position of another student relative to someone else. Play the game as in Part 1, with the following variation.

▶ When the music stops and students hold up placards, call upon someone *without* a placard to respond for a student holding a placard. (Max says, "Tomas is to the right of Robin.")

▶ Responding students may change position if such a change will help them respond appropriately. @

Developing Visual/Spatial Thinking Abilities

In Part 2 of the games students must put themselves in another's position and describe position from a viewpoint other than their own. Developing such visual/spatial skills is crucial to the understanding of many science concepts. Students will have opportunities for practicing these skills throughout this module. @

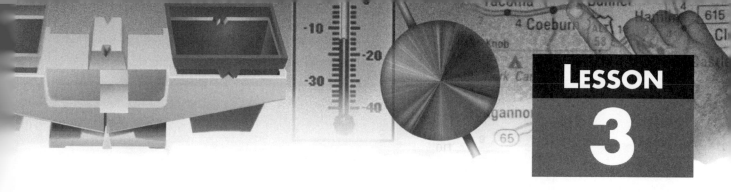

Where From C.Q.?

The class uses a stand-up figure of C.Q. and a yarn quadrant to describe students' positions in terms of two directions from C.Q. Then, each team places a crayon on the quadrant as directed by their Put-It-In-Position card. After all crayons are in position, teams write a description of the position of any six crayons of their choice. Then, the class checks the accuracy of each teams' descriptions and the placement of each crayon with the Put-It-In-Position cards.

Estimated Time:
2 class sessions

Purpose: To create a need for students to describe the position of objects with greater accuracy

To provide an opportunity for students to explore position as described in terms of two directions from an object

OUTCOMES	ASSESSMENT INDICATORS
	Students show they have achieved the outcome by:
Conceptual	
Students recognize that they describe the location of objects in relation to other objects.	• describing objects' positions in terms of two directions from C.Q., such as **in front/back of**, and to the **left/right of**, and • placing themselves and objects (crayons) in positions described in terms of two directions from C.Q.
Students recognize the need for describing the position of objects with greater accuracy.	• considering how to describe the positions of two students in front of C.Q. to indicate that, although both students are in front of C.Q., one student is to the left and the other student is to the right.
Scientific Inquiry	
Understandings Students become aware of the importance of describing things as accurately as possible in science.	• discussing why it is more helpful to describe an object's position by saying "to the right of C.Q. and in back of C.Q." rather than "to the right of C.Q."
Collaborative	
Students do their jobs.	• in addition to the responsibilities of manager, tracker, and messenger, individual students either –put the crayon in position, or –check the position of the crayon, or –read the Put-It-In-Position card to the class.

Supplies

For the Entire Class:
- BLM 3-1, *Put-It-In-Position Cards*
- BLM 3-2, *Put-It-In-Position Record Page*
- 1 piece of blue yarn, 8–10 feet long
- 1 piece of green yarn, 8–10 feet long
- chart paper
- markers, non-toxic: red, yellow, and a dark color
- masking tape
- 4 sheets of construction paper 12 inches × 18 inches, one red, one yellow, two other light colors
- large stand-up figure of C.Q.
- 10 crayons, one of each of the following colors—red, yellow, pink, orange, blue, black, brown, green, purple, and white
- writing paper
- scissors

For Each Team of 3:
- 1 crayon
- 1 Put-It-In-Position card
- 1 copy of BLM 3-2, *Put-It-In-Position Record Page*
- pencils

Before You Begin

▶ Review the student pages for this lesson.

▶ Review *Information for the Teacher* for background on this lesson.

▶ For this lesson, students will need a yarn quadrant on the floor in the group area, as diagramed below. Initially, tape only the length of green yarn to the floor, and add the blue yarn in Strategy 7.

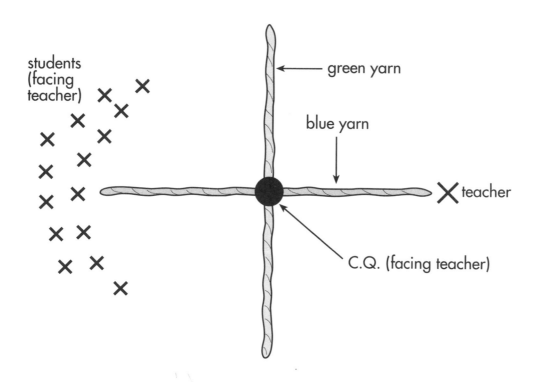

▶ Fold the sheets of construction paper in half lengthwise to make self-standing signs for the quadrants, but do not place them at this time.
  • Write "to the left of" on the yellow sign.
  • Write "to the right of" on the red sign.
  • Write "in front of" on one of the remaining two signs, and write "in back of" on the other.

▶ Make two copies of BLM 3-1, *Put-It-In-Position Cards*. Cut one copy apart at the lines, and save the other copy to check students' descriptions of position at the end of the lesson.

▶ Gather the crayons as specified in the supply list.

Teaching Strategies   Session 1

1. Introducing the Lesson

▶ Assemble students in a large semicircle in the group area as diagramed in *Before You Begin.*

- Show the class the stand-up figure of C.Q.
- Explain that they will use C.Q. to find out more about describing position.
- Place C.Q. at midpoint on the length of green yarn, facing front with his back to the students.

2. Positioning People in Front/Back of C.Q.

▶ Select a student to stand somewhere around C.Q. and the green yarn.

- Ask the class to describe the student's position relative to C.Q.
- Based on the response, place the appropriate *in front/back of* construction paper sign in the area.
- Have another student place the remaining *in front/back of* sign in the appropriate area.

▶ Invite several students to stand either in front or in back of C.Q.

- One at a time, ask each of the standing students, "Where are you from C.Q.?"
- Have each student describe where he or she is standing from C.Q.

Help students continue to develop the idea of describing position in relation to another object by encouraging students to describe their location in relation to C.Q. If students say, "I'm in back", ask, "What are you in back of?"

- Have the standing students change their position and have several seated students describe where the standing students are from C.Q.

This should be brief as students probably will not have any difficulty describing in front/back of.

3. Presenting to the Left/Right of C.Q.

▶ Introduce *to the left/right of* C.Q. with questions like these.

- What other directions did we use in the *Who Is Where Game* to describe someone's position?
- Which is C.Q.'s left hand and which is his right?

▶ One at a time, color code C.Q.'s hands.

- Color the front and back of C.Q.'s left hand yellow.
- Explain that you have colored it **L**emon yellow to remind them that it is C.Q.'s **L**eft hand.
- Color C.Q.'s **R**ight hand with the **R**eally **R**ed marker.
- See if students can guess why you chose red for that hand.

4. Completing the Quadrant

▶ Replace C.Q. midpoint on the green yarn and introduce the length of blue yarn.

- Have the class help you decide where to place the length of blue yarn to help students know just where C.Q.'s left or right side begins.
- Tape the blue yarn perpendicular to the green yarn at a 90 degree angle so it crosses at the mid-point of the green yarn, and place C.Q. back in his original position.

5. Positioning People to the Left/Right of C.Q.

▶ Provide an opportunity for students to describe positions as to the left/right of C.Q. with strategies such as these.

- Select several students to stand anywhere they want on the yarn quadrant.
- One at a time, ask students, "Are you standing to the left or right of C.Q.?"

Students should tell whether they are standing to C.Q.'s right or to his left. If students have difficulty, point out C.Q.'s hands and the blue yarn.

- Have the students sit down and invite several others to stand on the quadrant.

- Call upon students in the class to describe whether each student is standing to the left or to the right of C.Q.

- If seated students have difficulty putting themselves in another's place to describe position, remind them of the technique in Lesson 2, "seeing with their mind's eye."

6. Introducing Position in Terms of Two Directions from C.Q.

▶ Introduce the need for describing position in terms of two directions from C.Q.

- Select one student (student x) to stand in one quadrant in front of C.Q. and another (student y) to stand in the other front quadrant.

- Point out that both students are standing in front of C.Q.

- Ask students if both students are standing in the same position from C.Q.

- If student responses differ, encourage students to discuss the question with their classmates until they realize that the students are not in the same position from C.Q.

- Challenge students to describe the positions of students x and y so that others would know just where x and y are from C.Q. Encourage students to discuss their ideas with those around them before making suggestions for the class.

- If students have difficulty, ask questions to help them recognize that they can describe position in two directions from C.Q.

7. Reinforcing the Idea of Describing Position in Two Directions from C.Q.

▶ Give students opportunities to position themselves from C.Q. in terms of two directions.

- Ask a volunteer to stand in back of C.Q., and to his left.

- One at a time, describe other positions in terms of two directions, and have volunteers respond by standing in those positions. ("Angelina, stand in front of C.Q. and to his right.")

▶ Provide an opportunity for students to use two directions in describing position relative to C.Q.

- Invite some students who have not previously participated to stand anywhere on the quadrant.

- Ask the class to describe the students' positions, one at a time, from C.Q.

Students should respond with two directions, for example, "Blake is to the right and in front of C.Q." or "Blake is to the right of C.Q. He is in front of C.Q., too." If students have difficulty, point out the yarn and C.Q.'s hands. Encourage describing students to imagine themselves in Blake's place.

8. Closing the Session

▶ Ask students what they have been learning about.

Students will probably focus their responses on C.Q. and standing different places on the yarn quadrant.

▶ Refocus students on the idea of describing position with questions such as the following.

Because students are still exploring the concept of describing position, don't expect them to express their ideas clearly at this time. Nor should you explain at length if students do not seem to be connecting their activities with the quadrant to describing relative position. It is enough to raise the question, "Why have we been doing this?"

EXPLORE 29

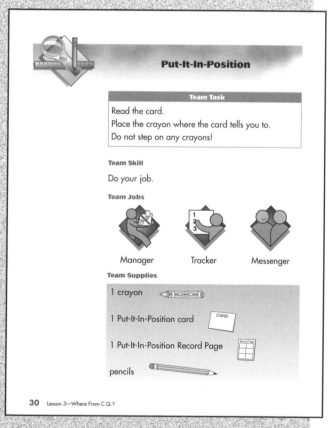

- Why were you standing around the yarn and C.Q.?
- What did you do besides stand around the yarn and C.Q.?
- How did you use C.Q. to help you describe where you or someone else was?
- What do you call *where* someone is? (Position)
- How did you use C.Q. and the yarn to describe someone's position?
- Why is it important to be able to describe someone's or something's position?

▶ Tell the students that they will use what they have learned to play a game in the next session.

If possible, leave the yarn quadrant in place for the next session. In the meantime, interested students can continue to use it.

★ See student pages 29–32

Teaching Strategies   Session 2

9. Playing the Game, *Put-It-In-Position*—Team Task

▶ Remind the class that they will use what they learned in Session 1 to play a game using C.Q. and the yarn.

▶ Introduce the student pages and discuss the task as necessary.

- If you have dismantled the yarn quadrant, have some students set it up again and place C.Q. in position.
- Assign teams to their workstations, and have them begin.

Circulate among teams, listen to their conversations, and make notes. This is an excellent opportunity for you to assess the developing understanding of individual students. Continue listening, taking notes, and interacting with students as they describe the position of crayons on their record pages in the next strategy.

- After teams place their crayons, remind them to choose any 6 crayons and describe the position of the crayons on their record page.
- When they finish their descriptions, direct teams to sit together in the group area.
- Encourage teams to discuss *Checking Understanding* as they wait.

10. Processing the Game

▶ When all teams have finished, process the activity by checking the position for each crayon, one at a time.

- Ask the class to look at the (red) crayon, and tell where it is from C.Q.

Teams should use their written descriptions of the positions of the six crayons to respond. Members of the team that placed the crayon should not participate until it is time to read their Put-It-In-Position card.

- Have the corresponding team's reader read the Put-It-In-Position card.
- Ask the class if the directions on the card were the same as the descriptions the teams gave.

- If not, encourage the team to justify their placement of the crayon and the members of the class to justify their description of the crayon's position. If there is still no consensus, redirect students' attention to the crayon and ask: "Is the crayon in front or in back of C.Q.? Is it to the left or the right of C.Q.? If so, what is the position of the crayon?"

Directions for Put-It-In-Position

1. Get a card and the matching crayon.
2. Read your card.
3. Talk about where you should put the crayon until everyone agrees on the position.

4. Decide **who** will do these jobs.
   ▶ Put the crayon in position.
   ▶ Check to make sure the crayon is placed where your team agreed.
   ▶ Read the card to the class.

5. After you decide on a job for each teammate, do your jobs.
   ▶ Put the crayon in position.
   ▶ Check the position of the crayon.
   ▶ Read the card when it is your team's turn.
6. While you wait for your team's turn, do the Put-It-In-Position Record Page.

Be careful. Do not step on any crayons!

Checking Understanding

With your team, talk about these things.
1. You described the position of all of the crayons from _____ .
2. Which is more helpful to describe an object's position?
   ▶ The object is to the right of C.Q.
   ▶ The object is to the right of C.Q. and in back of C.Q?
3. Why do you think so?

Assessment Strategies

Lesson 3 has enabled you to assess students' developing understanding of describing position in terms of two directions from an object.

- You have observed students position themselves and discuss and describe position from C.Q. in the first session.
- You have observed teams discuss and decide where to place their crayons on the yarn quadrant.
- You have observed and interacted with teams as they recorded the position of crayons on the yarn quadrant.
- You have observed students during the class discussion as they question and justify the position and description of position of the crayons.

11. Continuing Assessment

▶ Have students discuss the questions in *Checking Understanding* with their teammates.

You might decide to have teams discuss and individual students record their answers in their own science folders before the class discussion.

▶ Assess students' progress in describing objects relative to other objects by randomly calling on students to share the results of their team's discussion with the class. Include viewpoints from several teams for each question.

Question 1: Students should recognize that they described the position of all of the crayons from C.Q.

Questions 2 and 3: Students should realize that describing position in terms of two directions from C.Q. is more helpful because using both directions helps pinpoint the position. However, do not be concerned about students expressing a "correct answer" at this time. Regard the discussion as an opportunity for students to express their ideas at this point in the module.

Information for the Teacher

The first session of this lesson introduces students to the idea of describing an object's position in terms of two directions from C.Q. ("in front of and to the right of C.Q."). Because Session 1 presents a conventional way of doing something (describing position in terms of two directions), it is a rather structured and teacher-directed whole-class activity. In the second session, however, students are able to explore the idea with their teammates by doing a team task and talking about what they do.

The visual/spatial skills that students use in this lesson progress gradually in difficulty from those skills in the previous lesson. First, students describe their own position in terms of two directions from C.Q. Then, in the same terms, they describe the position of other students and objects. ◉

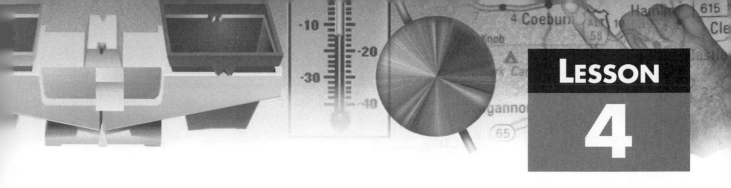

Where From What?

Estimated Time:
2 class sessions

C.Q. and I.O. introduce a torn treasure map, and teams consider the problem of what they need to know to find, or describe, the position of an object like the treasure. The students use their common experiences from Lessons 1–3 to help them develop an explanation for describing an object's position relative to another object. Once students can express their ideas about the concept, the teacher introduces the term **reference object**. The class reviews the chart of helpful words to see if it addressed the idea of reference objects and modifies the chart as necessary. Then, teams play *I Spy* with a focus on the reference objects.

Purpose: To allow students to express their understanding of describing position relative to another object

To provide a useful term after students have expressed their idea in their own language

OUTCOMES	ASSESSMENT INDICATORS
	Students show they have achieved the outcome by:
Conceptual	
Students understand that they describe the position of objects in relation to other objects.	• identifying the reference objects they used to describe the position of other objects, • explaining that C.Q. and I.O. need to identify a reference object in order to find the treasure, and • generalizing that describing position requires reference to another object.
Scientific Inquiry	
Abilities Students use data to construct a reasonable explanation.	• discussing and recalling that, in Lessons 1–3, they described the position of objects in relation to other objects, and • using the information from Lessons 1–3 to explain why C.Q. and I.O. cannot find the treasure without a reference object.
Collaborative	
Students share and take turns.	• taking turns expressing their ideas about C.Q.'s and I.O.'s problem before recording their own ideas in their science folders, and • sharing responsibility for helping teammates express their ideas in a class discussion.

Supplies

For the Entire Class:
- 1 pair of cardboard binoculars from Lesson 1
- lengths of yarn on floor as used in Lesson 3
- large stand-up model of C.Q.
- class chart of helpful words from Lesson 1
- marker, non-toxic
- 1 crayon or another object
- chart paper

For Each Team of 3:
- science folder for each teammate
- writing paper
- cardboard binoculars
- pencils

Before You Begin

▶ Review the student pages for this lesson.

▶ Review *Who Explains What?* in *Information for the Teacher.*

▶ Before Session 1, post the class chart of helpful words from Lesson 1 and 2 near the group area.

▶ Before Session 2, do these things.
- Replace the yarn quadrant and C.Q. in the group area.
- Write the incomplete sentence "The treasure is buried beside the..." at the top of a sheet of chart paper.

Teaching Strategies   Session 1

★ See student pages 33–36

1. Reviewing Data from Lessons 1-3

▶ Invite students to bring their science folders and assemble in the group area.

▶ Point out and remind students of the class chart of helpful words.

- What kinds of words did we write on this chart?

- What did these words help us describe? (position or where something is)

- When you describe something's position, what are you describing? (where something is)

▶ Briefly review with students Lesson 1, *I Spy,* by asking questions such as these.

- In *I Spy,* what were you describing the position of? (things or objects)

- How did you describe the position of objects in the classroom? You described where the objects were *from what?* (from other things or objects)

▶ Continue the same kind of brief review with Lessons 2 and 3.

- Tell me about the *Who Is Where Game* we played in Lesson 2.

- Did we add words or phrases on this chart from that game? Which ones? (in front/back of, to the left/right of)

- In the game, you described where your classmates were *from what?* (from me, from other students)

- In *Put-It-In-Position,* you placed the crayons where *from what?* (from C.Q.)

▶ Tell students that teams will be using what they learned about describing position in the next team task.

2. Explaining the Problem—Team Task

▶ Introduce the student pages and have teams begin the task.

It is likely that students will have more experience in identifying/choosing answers than in discussing and comparing possible answers. Circulate among the teams, listen to their conversation, and make notes. If a team has difficulty getting started, or stalls, redirect them with comments and questions about how they described position in Lessons 1-3. Do not expect students to reach a well thought-out conclusion before the class discussion at the end of the lesson.

▶ Although this is a team activity, provide the structure for individual students to begin developing their own explanations.

LESSON 4

Where From What?

You have been describing the position of objects — where they are. Where is the buried treasure? I.O. and C.Q. want to find it!

This map says that the treasure is buried beside....... I can't read that part, C.Q. The map is torn.

EXPLAIN 33

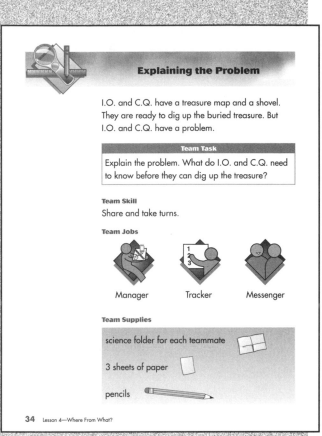

Explaining the Problem

I.O. and C.Q. have a treasure map and a shovel. They are ready to dig up the buried treasure. But I.O. and C.Q. have a problem.

Team Task

Explain the problem. What do I.O. and C.Q. need to know before they can dig up the treasure?

Team Skill
Share and take turns.

Team Jobs

Manager   Tracker   Messenger

Team Supplies

science folder for each teammate

3 sheets of paper

pencils

34   Lesson 4—Where From What?

- Encourage teams to make sure all teammates express their ideas.
- Emphasize that teammates *may* disagree.
- Encourage students to explain why they think so.
- Encourage students to ask others, "Why do you think so?"

▶ Note examples of teammates sharing ideas so that you can share them with the class.

3. Closing the Session

▶ After teams complete the task, collect students' science folders. Inform students that they will share ideas in the next session.

▶ To help you prepare for the class discussion in the next session, review the science folders for insight into students' developing understanding.

Directions for Explaining the Problem

1. Look at the treasure map.

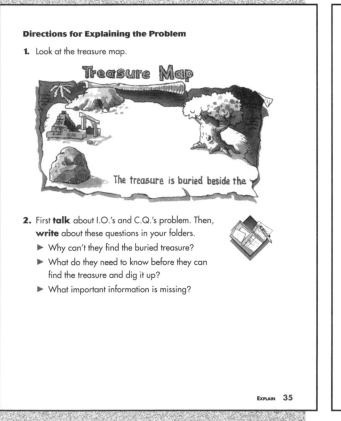

The treasure is buried beside the

2. First **talk** about I.O.'s and C.Q.'s problem. Then, **write** about these questions in your folders.
- ▶ Why can't they find the buried treasure?
- ▶ What do they need to know before they can find the treasure and dig it up?
- ▶ What important information is missing?

EXPLAIN   35

The treasure might be buried anywhere!

3. Look at the treasure map again and do these things.
- ▶ Imagine **where** the treasure is buried.
- ▶ Tell where the treasure might be buried by finishing the sentence on the torn map.

The treasure is buried beside the

▶ Write your finished sentence in your folder. Be ready to share the ideas in your science folder with the class.

36   Lesson 4—Where From What?

Teaching Strategies   Session 2

4. Understanding the Role of a Reference Object in Describing Position

▶ Assemble students in the group area with their science folders.

▶ Randomly call upon members of several teams to tell what C.Q. and I.O. need to know before they can find the treasure. If students have difficulty expressing their thoughts, encourage their teammates to help them.

Through discussion and questions, help students realize that I.O. and C.Q. do not have a reference object to use in finding the treasure. They have the descriptor, "beside," but they don't know which object the treasure is beside. I.O. and C.Q. would have to dig around the cave, rock, tree, stone ruins, and so forth, in hopes of finding the treasure.

▶ Invite students to share their finished sentences from their science folders. List students' responses on the chart paper under the unfinished sentence.

Point out the reminder figure on page 36, saying, "The treasure might be buried anywhere!" Emphasize that there is no one right answer—only imaginary answers.

5. Testing Ideas

▶ Invite students to test their ideas about what information C.Q. and I.O. need to find the treasure. Use strategies similar to the following.

- Direct students' attention to C.Q. and the yarn quadrant.
- Place a crayon in a quadrant.
- Ask a team to describe the position of the crayon and write their description on the board.
- Check to see if all teams agree with the description.

If there is a difference of opinion, discuss the differences until the class reaches consensus on the description.

- Ask what students needed to know to describe the crayon's position.

If students reply that they needed to know where the crayon was, direct their attention to the description on the board. Help them realize that they need to know the crayon's position from C.Q. with questions such as, "What else do you need?" "The crayon is where from what?"

6. Introducing the Term, "Reference Object"

▶ Once students begin to get the idea that they described the crayon's position relative to, compared to, or *where from C.Q.*, introduce the term **reference object**, with strategies similar to the following.

For primary students, you will probably need to substitute the phrase "compared to" for the phrase "in relation to."

- Point out that students described the crayon's position in relation to C.Q. *(to the left of C.Q.; in front of C.Q.).*
- Explain that people describe the position of objects in relation to something else.
- Explain that people call *what* they are using to compare position to, like C.Q., a **reference object**.
- Explain that C.Q. is a **reference object** because the students described the position of the crayon in relation to C.Q.

7. Changing the Reference Object

▶ Remove C.Q. and direct a student to stand in C.Q.'s place.

- Ask the class to describe the position of the crayon.

The description should be exactly the same, except students will describe the crayon compared (or relative) to the student rather than to C.Q.

- Ask the class to identify the reference object that they used.

Assessment Strategies

During this lesson, students have done these things.

- They have expressed their understanding of the role of reference objects relative to describing the position of other objects.

- They have used data from their activities and discussions in Lessons 1-3 to help them develop their understanding.

Because you observed teams, interacted with individual students, and reviewed their science folders, you should be able to clearly assess their understanding *up to this point.* Be aware, however, that some students might not "get it" until the close of the lesson or beyond.

8. Reviewing the List of Helpful Words

▶ Direct students' attention to the list of helpful words, and invite students to add to the list.

- Compare the chart of helpful words to the chart of students' phrases completing the unfinished sentence from the treasure map.

- If the first chart did not contain any reference objects, point out that I.O. and C.Q. had direction words, but they needed a reference object also.

- If the list of helpful words contained reference objects, have students circle them.

- Invite students to help solve the problem of noting reference objects on the first chart.

Students might choose to add the term **reference object** *to the chart. They might decide to add a variety of reference objects. Implement whatever solution they suggest, if it has appropriate meaning for students.*

9. Returning to the Problem of the Buried Treasure

▶ Connect the term, **reference object**, to the problem of finding the buried treasure. Ask students what a reference object has to do with I.O.'s and C.Q.'s problem.

▶ Continue the discussion by pointing out the unfinished sentence and completing phrases on the second chart and asking several students to circle a word that could be a reference object.

Students should quickly realize that all of the words that complete the unfinished sentence could be reference objects that describe the position of the treasure. The treasure could be beside the cave, the ruins, the palm tree, etc. Continue to reinforce that the reference object is what *you are describing the position of the treasure from.*

10. Continuing to Assess Understanding

▶ Close the session by inviting teams to use their binoculars to play a variation of the game, *I Spy.* The new version requires students to identify the reference object they use in their description.

- Use your binoculars to model the game. After a student correctly guesses an object based on your description of its position (as in the game in Lesson 1) ask, "What was my reference object?"

In some descriptions, students might use multiple reference objects. For example, a student might say, "I spy an object that is on top of the file cabinet beside the red book." Both file cabinet and red book are reference objects. Don't raise the issue at this time, but address it if some students are perceptive enough to recognize multiple reference objects.

- After students seem to understand the change to the original game, give teams an opportunity to play *I Spy,* either now or later.

★ See student page 37

▶ Introduce and assign *Checking Understanding* in the student guide.

▶ When students complete the individual task, collect their science folders and review them.

Students should have circled the reference object in their sentence and drawn any appropriate object from the treasure map.

Checking Understanding

After you share your ideas with the class, do these things.

  ▶ Look at the sentence you finished in your science folder.

  ▶ Circle the reference object in the sentence.

  ▶ Look at the treasure map. Draw something else from the map that could be a reference object.

EXPLAIN **37**

Information for the Teacher

Who Explains What?

The purpose of this lesson is to provide an opportunity for students to reflect on the activities in Lessons 1-3, draw some conclusions about how they describe where objects are, and express their understanding of the concept of relative position.

The main idea is for students to understand that they describe an object's position relative to (compared to) other objects. The term **reference object** is useful in communicating, but the concept is more important than the term. If students seem to understand the concept of reference object, don't be concerned if they do not remember the term. @

More Than Direction

Pairs of teams use distance as well as direction to play a game called *Find the Message.* Teams set up their own yarn quadrants and choose one team member to be C.Q., the reference object. Teams place paper cups upside down in every section of their quadrant and hide a message under one of the cups. Each team's measurer finds out how many toe-heel steps there are from C.Q. to the specific cup, and each team's writer records the directions. After teams trade directions and quadrants, students see if the directions enable them to find the message. Then, the *Find-the-Crab's-Name Page* challenges students to apply what they have learned.

Estimated Time: 1 or more class sessions (See *Before You Begin*)

Purpose: To establish a need for students to describe the position of an object with greater accuracy.

OUTCOMES	ASSESSMENT INDICATORS
	Students show they have achieved the outcome by:
Conceptual	
Students extend their understanding of describing position relative to other objects by adding distance to their descriptions.	• describing a specific cup's position from C.Q. in terms of distance as well as direction, • finding the specific cup using written directions that include both distance and direction from C.Q., and • explaining what information they will need to find the letter of the crab's name on the *Find-the-Crab's-Name Page*.
Scientific Inquiry	
Understandings Students recognize the importance of describing things as accurately as possible in science.	• expressing that they are unable to distinguish which of three cups holds a message in terms of directions only, • expressing the advantage of describing the position of a specific cup in terms of distance as well as direction, and • expressing what they mean by "good" directions.
Collaborative	
Students do their jobs.	• alternately assuming responsibility for the job of measurer, writer, and C.Q. (reference object).

Supplies

For the Entire Class:

- BLM 5-1, *Find-the-Crab's-Name Page*
- BLM 5-2, How to *Find the Crab's Name Page*
- yarn lengths as in Lessons 3-4
- 12 paper cups, 4 ounce size
- chart paper or blackboard
- marker, non-toxic or chalk
- drawing paper
- 1 box of small paper clips, 1 inch size (Do not substitute another size)
- scissors
- 2 rubber bands, one each of red and yellow
- pencil

For Each Team of 3:

- 1 copy of BLM 5-1, *Find-the-Crab's-Name Page*
- 1 copy of BLM 5-2, How to *Find the Crab's Name Page*
- 1 length of green yarn, 2 meters long
- 1 length of blue yarn, 2 meters long
- 12 paper cups, 4 ounce size
- masking tape
- 1 red rubber band, medium width
- 1 yellow rubber band, medium width
- scissors
- drawing paper
- science folder for each teammate
- pencils

Before You Begin

▶ Review student pages for this lesson.

▶ Review the following sections in *Information for the Teacher.*

- *Guidelines on Scheduling and Necessary Preparations for the Find the Message Game*
- *Guidelines on the Find-the-Crab's-Name Activity*

▶ Duplicate the following pages.

- Make 1 copy of BLM 5-1, *Find-the-Crab's-Name Page,* for each team.
- Make 1 copy of BLM 5-2, *How to Find the Crab's Name Page,* for each team.

▶ Two teams will need to pair to play *Find the Message.* Decide which teams to pair.

▶ Just before the lesson, make the following preparations so that you will be able to demonstrate *Find the Message* for the class.

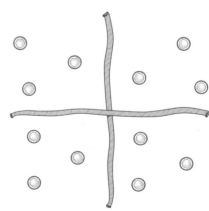

- Set up the yarn quadrant in the group area, as in Lessons 3-4.
- Place 3 cups, at least two footsteps apart, in each quadrant. Two of the cups should be about the same distance from the intersection of the yarn.
- Write a message for the class on a half sheet of paper, fold it tightly, and place it under one of the cups.

Teaching Strategies   Session 1

1. Introducing the *Find the Message* Game

▶ Assemble students in the group area and position them on the yarn quadrant as they were in Lessons 3 and 4.

▶ Invite students to find out more about describing position by looking for a hidden message.

- Select a volunteer to stand on the quadrant as C.Q., with a yellow rubber band on the left wrist and a red rubber band on the right.

- Point out the cups on the quadrant and tell the class that you have hidden a message under one of them.

- Ask students what they need to know before they can find the message.

Students will likely respond that they need to know where *the cup is from C.Q. (in front/back of, to the right/left of).*

▶ Describe the quadrant in which the cup is located by two directions from C.Q., just as teams described the position of crayons in Lesson 4.

Use a description such as, "The cup is in back of C.Q. and to his left."

▶ Ask students if they can tell, from your directions, *which* of the cups has the message.

Students should realize that they do not have enough information to identify the specific cup.

▶ Focus students' attention on the value of describing *distance* as well as *direction* from C.Q., with strategies such as the following.

- Challenge the class to give you suggestions for describing the position of the cup with the message.

Students might come up with the idea of distance as well as direction from

C.Q. *If not, ask guiding questions to elicit this response.*

- If students suggest describing distance only as nearer to or farther from C.Q., point out that some of the cups are about the same distance from C.Q.

- Ask students how you could describe more accurately the distance of the cup from C.Q.

Students will likely respond that you could measure the distance. They might suggest various measuring tools.

- Point out that, long ago, people used their feet as measurement tools and suggest that the class count toe-heel steps to measure the distance.

- If students protest that their feet differ in size, suggest that they try it and see how it works.

Even though the students' feet will vary some in size, the measurements should be accurate enough for students to be able to find a specific cup from the description.

2. Demonstrating the *Find the Message* Game

▶ Demonstrate how to measure distance from C.Q.

- Select a volunteer to be the measurer.

- Have C.Q. move aside so that the measurer can begin from the intersection of the yarn.

- Direct the measurer to toe-heel along the yarn in front/back of C.Q. (the intersection of the yarn) as the class counts the steps.

- Say *STOP* when the measurer is opposite the specific cup and direct her/him to stay in that spot.

▶ Show the class how to record directions to the specific cup with strategies such as these.

- Ask how many steps there are in front/back of C.Q. to the specific cup.

LESSON 5

More Than Direction

You have been describing something's position as "to the left of" and "in front of" a reference object. What if you know directions like these, but they are not enough? How can you find what you are looking for?

There is a message under one of the cups that is in back of C.Q. and to the right of C.Q. But **which** cup is the cup with the message?

I.O. knows the directions of the cup from C.Q. But there are 3 cups in back of C.Q. and to his right. What information would help I.O. find the right cup?

ELABORATE 39

Find the Message

Everyone needs good directions to be able to find something. Some directions or descriptions are better than others. See if your team writes good directions.

Ha! I don't need good directions to find you, C.Q!

Team Task

Hide a message under a cup. Write good directions to the cup.

Team Jobs

Manager   Tracker   Messenger

40   Lesson 5—More Than Direction

- Ask for suggestions on writing that part of the directions to the specific cup.
- Write the directions on the board (for example, Go 3 steps in back of C.Q.).
- Repeat the strategies to measure the distance to the left/right of C.Q., and complete the directions (for example, Go 2 steps to the left of C.Q.).

▶ Connect describing the position of the specific cup to the written directions, with strategies similar to the following.

- Select another student to follow the written directions and point out the specific cup.
- Ask the class if the directions could describe the position of any of the other cups.

If students think the directions describe the position of more than one cup, invite someone to follow the directions and find out.

- Invite a student to read the message in the cup.

★ See student pages 39–47

3. Setting Up Find the Message— Team Task

▶ Explain that teams will have their own yarn set-up. They will hide messages for other teams to find.

- Introduce the student pages and discuss as necessary.
- Assign a work area to each team, pair teams for trading directions and finding messages, and have teams begin the game.

Observe teams as they play the game. Record observations that might be useful in interviewing or assessing students. Question individuals or teams to assess students' understanding at this point in the module.

Team Skills

Do your job.

Team Supplies

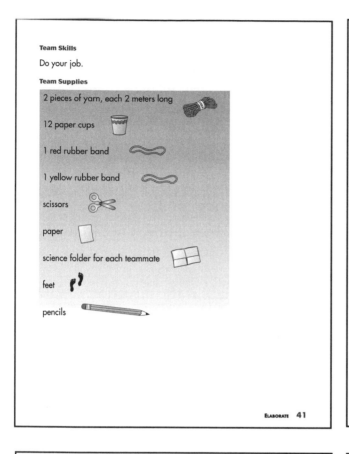

2 pieces of yarn, each 2 meters long

12 paper cups

1 red rubber band

1 yellow rubber band

scissors

paper

science folder for each teammate

feet

pencils

Directions for Finding the Message

1. Put the yarn on the floor.
  ▶ Put 3 cups upside down in each part.
  ▶ Be sure the cups are at least 2 footsteps apart.

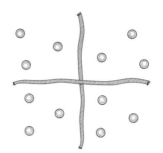

Don't forget where you put the message!

2. Make a message for the other team.
  ▶ Cut the paper in half.
  ▶ Write a short message on one half of the paper.
  ▶ Fold the message small enough to fit under a cup.
  ▶ Hide the message under a cup.

3. For the first game, decide **who will do each job**.
  ▶ Someone will be **C.Q.** Your job is to be the reference object.

I will wear a red rubber band on my right hand, and a yellow on my left. But, if I am the reference object, where do I stand?

Toe-heel, toe-heel, toe-heel. 3 steps in front. Now, how many steps to the right?

  ▶ Someone will be the **measurer**. Your job is to measure how far to the cup in steps.

  ▶ Someone will be the **writer**. Your job is to write good directions to the cup with the message.

Go 3 steps in front of C.Q. Now, how many steps to the right?

4. Now, do your jobs.
  ▶ **C.Q.** puts on the rubber bands, stands on the yarn, and stays there.
  ▶ The **measurer** measures how many steps to the right cup with the message.
  ▶ The **writer** writes the directions to the cup with the message.

5. Your team's directions describe where the cup with the message is from C.Q. It should look something like this.

Go 3 steps in front of C.Q.

Go 3 steps to the right of C.Q.

ELABORATE   **45**

Assessment Strategies

You have assessed students' developing understanding through your observations and interactions. At this point in the lesson, you have an indication of students who do, or do not, understand the following ideas.

- Accurately describing the position of objects is important because it enables people to find things.
- One way to describe position more accurately or precisely is to describe distance as well as direction from the reference object.

6. Trade directions with the other team and try to find their message.

▶ Two teammates go to the other team's station, but C.Q. stays at your station.

▶ Follow the other team's directions.

▶ If the directions are good, you will find the cup with the message and read the message.

46   Lesson 5—More Than Direction

7. Go back to your station and play Game 2, if you have time.

Remember, give everyone a turn to do the jobs of C.Q., the measurer, and the writer.

ELABORATE   **47**

4. Continuing to Assess Students' Understanding

★ See student page 48

▶ After teams play several rounds of the game, introduce *Checking Understanding*.

- Discuss as necessary. Make sure students understand that they will talk about the questions with their teams, but record their ideas in their own science folders.

- As teams work, take advantage of this opportunity to observe, to interact, and to record specific information for assessing student understanding.

- Do not distribute the *How to Find the Crab's Name Page* until after all students complete their science folders and return them to you.

Students will need to discuss and reflect on questions 1 and 2 without the distraction of having the How to Find the Crab's Name Page.

Checking Understanding

Talk about these questions with your team. Then, write your answers in your science folder.

1. Your team task was to write "good" directions to the cup.
   ▶ What do people mean by "good" directions?
   ▶ In the task, what words could you use instead of "good"?

2. Look at the Find-the-Crab's-Name Page.
   ▶ What information would you need to find the letters of the crab's name?
   ▶ Make up "good" sample directions to one letter that might be in the crab's name.

3. When you are finished with your science folder, do the How To Find the Crab's Name Page with your team.

48   Lesson 5—More Than Direction

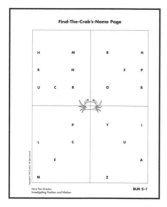

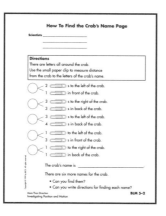

Information for the Teacher

∙∙

Guidelines on Scheduling and Necessary Preparations for the Find the Message Game

In this lesson, each team will set up and use their own small, yarn quadrant to play *Find the Message*. The team quadrants are 2 meters by 2 meters. Decide if you have enough space for teams to play in the classroom. If not, consider the following alternatives.

- Extend the space in the classroom by using the hallway.

- Plan an alternate location, such as a gym, cafeteria, or common area. If you decide to have teams play outdoors, consider the effect of the wind on the paper cups.

- Rather than having all teams play in the classroom at once, schedule only a few teams to play at a time. If you decide to proceed with this plan, arrange classroom space and adjust the team supplies accordingly.

If you have enough space for all teams to play concurrently, make the following preparations.

- Cut, or have students cut, ten 2-meter lengths each of blue and green yarn.

- Plan space for each team to use a set of 2 lengths of yarn to set up its own quadrant. @

Guidelines on the Find-the-Crab's-Name Activity

Attach or make available, three small paper clips for each team. Students will use the paper clips with the *How To Find the Crab's Name Page*. Initially, each team will receive one copy of BLM 5-1, *Find-the-Crab's-Name Page*. The three teammates in each team will share the one page. First, they will use the page to discuss and answer Question 2 in *Checking Understanding*. Students might recognize that they would need to know the distance and direction of each letter from the crab (how far in front of the crab, and how far to the right of the crab.) Students might suggest a unit of measure, such as thumbs or pennies. Then, when all teammates return their science folders to you, teams will use the page in combination with the *How To Find the Crab's Name Page* to complete the activity. The directions on BLM 5-2 help students find the crab's name, Cammy. There are six additional names (Chuck, Cleo, Pincher, Crabby, Charlie, Clipper.) Students can find the names and then write directions for other students to find the names. Interested students might want to develop similar activity pages. @

Where Is "Here"?

Students consider how people find and describe a position without C.Q. and the yarn sections. They think about everyday applications such as addresses and maps. Students help the teacher make a simple map of the classroom. Then teams draw their own basic maps of the playground and use the maps to play the *You Are Here Game*.

Purpose: To help students connect describing relative position to their daily lives

To allow students to represent the positions of objects graphically

OUTCOMES	ASSESSMENT INDICATORS
	Students show they have achieved the outcome by:
Conceptual	
Students extend their understanding of describing position relative to other objects.	• considering real-world applications of describing position such as a map, an address, and an advertised description of location, and • making and using a map of the playground.
Students recognize that people can describe the position of objects graphically.	• making a map of the playground, and • marking their positions on the map at intervals as they move from place to place.
Collaborative	
Students stay with their team.	Students stay with their team as they play the *You Are Here Game*.

Supplies

For the Entire Class:
- chart paper
- marker, non-toxic
- masking tape
- extra drawing paper
- several pencils with erasers
- sticky pad, 1½ inches × 2 inches size
- sticky pad, 3 inches × 3 inches size
- 1 holder or tote bag to hold the extra paper, pencils, and tape
- 1 whistle, bell, or another noise-making device
- 1 map, as simple as possible
- 1 envelope, addressed to a residence
- 1 advertisement, describing the location of a business in relation to something else (for example, *"next to City Park"* or *"one block in back of City Mall"*)
- fire escape route map from the classroom to the exit

For Each Team of 3:
- 1 tray
- 1 sheet of drawing paper, 8½ inches × 11 inches
- 1 sheet of construction paper
- 1 sticky note, 1½ inches × 2 inches size
- masking tape
- pencils with erasers

Before You Begin

▶ Review student pages for this lesson.

▶ Review *Information for the Teacher* for *Directions for the You Are Here Game.*

▶ Plan a time when the class can use the playground without sharing it with other students. If this is not possible, or the weather doesn't cooperate, plan an alternate area, such as the gym, for students to map, move about, and mark their positions on their maps.

▶ Before Session 2, do these things.

• Print "You are Here" and an arrow on 2 or 3 pages of the larger sticky pad. Put the arrow pointing to the edge opposite the sticky edge of each page you mark.

• Prepare a page from the smaller sticky pad for each team, plus a few extra pages. On each page, draw an arrow pointing toward the edge opposite the sticky edge, just as you did on the page from the larger pad. Do not, however, add the "You are Here."

• Choose a whistle, bell, or another noise-making device as a Go and Stop signal.

• Place extra masking tape, paper, a smaller pad of sticky notes, and pencils in the holder or tote bag.

Teaching Strategies Session 1

1. Describing Position in the Real World

▶ Assemble students in the group area and focus their attention on real world applications of describing position with strategies such as these.

- Remind students of previous lessons when they used C.Q. and the yarn to locate and describe position.
- Ask students to consider how people describe position without using C.Q. and the yarn.
- Ask students how people know how to find places like the library, park, school, or where someone lives.
- Briefly discuss their responses.

▶ One at a time, display the map, the address on the envelope, and the advertisement and briefly connect these examples to position and location.

▶ Show students the fire escape route map in the classroom.

- Have students point out their classroom on the map.
- Encourage students to explain briefly the use of the map in case of fire or a fire drill.

★ See student page 49

2. Introducing You Are Here as a Reference Object

▶ Introduce the idea of a mall map on the first page in the student guide.

- Question students to discover the extent of their experiences with similar maps.
- Discuss the use of such a map.
- Point out that the map in the student guide contains little detail.
- Discuss the amount of detail in a real mall map.

Where Is "Here"?

Have you ever used a map like this? How does the map help you know where you are? How does it help you find the place you want to go?

I don't remember exactly where the bookstore is. Maybe it is around the corner.

Wait, I.O. Let's use this map to find the bookstore.

ELABORATE 49

▶ Focus students' attention on the *You Are Here* spot on the map.

• Question students to determine their understanding of the phrase.

• Point out that the word "You" refers to the reference object in the *You Are Here* spot or place.

3. Mapping the Classroom

▶ Invite students to help you make a *You are Here* map of the classroom on chart paper.

• If you think it would be helpful for students, turn the chart paper lengthwise or widthwise to correspond with the dimensions of the classroom.

• Tell students that the map should be simple; it cannot show everything that is in the classroom.

• Have students suggest what kinds of things to add that would make the classroom map useful.

• As students suggest classroom features, encourage them to discuss and decide if you should add them to the map.

• Use student responses to draw a simple classroom map on the chart. Label as necessary.

Because you are modeling what teams will do in the team task on the playground in the second session, include minimal detail on the classroom map. See the simple map for an example.

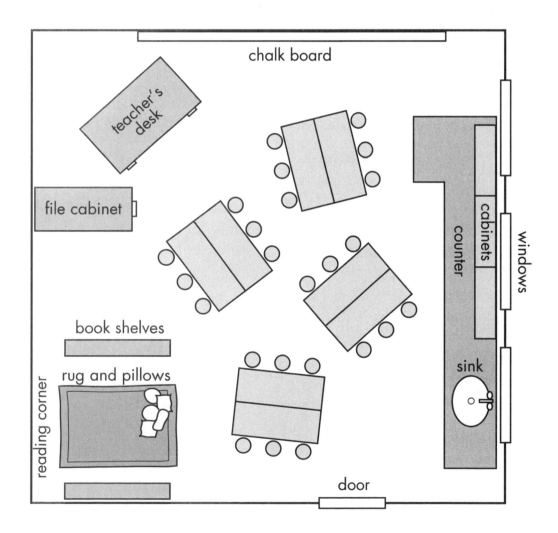

4. Establishing a You Are Here Place on the Classroom Map

▶ When you finish the simple classroom map, use it to probe students' understanding of *You Are Here* as a reference object.

- Have students sit closely together facing the same direction in the group area.
- Ask students what they see in front/back and to the right/left of them.
- Ask a student to post the *You Are Here* sticky note on the map in the same spot or position that the class is sitting.
- Establish with the class that the arrow points to what students see *in front of* them.

Note: On a mall map, the arrow that often accompanies the statement "You Are Here" usually points to the spot in the mall where you are but has no directional significance. This use of an arrow is different from the use of the arrow on the sticky pad. In this activity, the arrow points to the You Are Here *spot on the map but also points in the direction the students are facing.*

▶ Introduce the idea of changing the *You Are Here* position with strategies such as the following:

- Direct the students as a group to a different position in the classroom. Again students should be in a compact group facing the same direction.
- Ask a student to change the position of the sticky note on the map to match the class' new position.
- Point out that, because they changed their position in the classroom, students are at a different position on the class map.
- Ask students how the change in position changed what was in front/back and left/right of them.
- Ask students if the objects such as the teacher's desk actually changed position in the classroom. ("When you were sitting over there, you said my desk was in front of you. Now you say that it is to the right of you. What happened?")
- Continue changing the *You Are Here* position several times and asking similar questions.

Be sure to position students in one location other than the perimeter of the classroom, such as the center.

5. Closing the Session

▶ Tell the class that soon teams will draw their own map of the playground and use it to play the *You Are Here Game.*

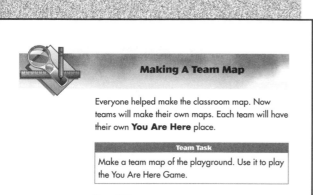

Making A Team Map

Everyone helped make the classroom map. Now teams will make their own maps. Each team will have their own **You Are Here** place.

Team Task
Make a team map of the playground. Use it to play the You Are Here Game.

Team Skill

Stay with your team.

Team Jobs

Manager   Tracker   Messenger

Team Supplies

1 tray

1 sheet of drawing paper

1 sheet of construction paper

masking tape

1 sticky note with an arrow on it

pencils with erasers

Directions for Making a Drawing Board and a Team Map

1. Before you go outside, do these things to make a drawing board.
  ▶ Turn your tray upside down.
  ▶ Put the construction paper on the bottom of the tray.

Teaching Strategies   Session 2

★ See student pages 50–52

6. Preparing for the Game

▶ Remind students of the previous session by briefly drawing their attention to the classroom map and the mall map.

▶ Introduce the task of *Making a Team Map* in the student guide.

▶ Emphasize the task and the purpose for students going outside.

▶ Establish *with* the class clear guidelines for appropriate behavior.

  • Have students describe what is acceptable behavior for the skill, "staying with your team."

  • Make sure you establish a signal for assembling the class outdoors so that, when necessary, you can review guidelines or instructions.

  • Introduce the Go signal and the Stop signal.

  • Have teams complete their drawing boards before going outdoors.

  • Tell students that you will take extra pencils, paper, tape, and an extra small pad of sticky notes outside.

7. Drawing Playground Maps

Take the class to a specific, well-defined position on the playground and have teams draw their maps.

Drawing playground maps will be easier for students if you position them in an easily recognized area, such as by a piece of playground equipment.

  • Visit each team, observe their maps, and assist students as necessary.

  • When teams complete their maps, have all students face the same direction.

► Ask questions such as the following to assess students' understanding of their position relative to other objects on the playground.

- Where are the swings from you?
- What is in back of you and to your left?
- Is anything in back of you?
- Is the slide directly in front of you?

► Direct students to place their sticky note on their team maps with the arrow distinguishing where they currently are on the map.

- Ask students which way the arrow on the note should point.
- Reinforce the idea that the arrow should point to what students see in front of them.

★ See student pages 53–55

8. Playing the *You Are Here Game*

► Briefly introduce the directions and invite students to play the *You Are Here Game.*

- Shortly after each stopping signal, visit several teams and observe the position of the sticky note on each map. Try to visit each team at least once.
- Question team members about their placement in relation to the objects on the playground and about the corresponding positions on their team map.

► Put the drawing paper on top of the construction paper.
► Then, tape the drawing and construction paper to the bottom of the tray.

All teammates should decide how to draw the map and take turns drawing it.

2. When you go outside, draw a map of the playground.
► Do not put everything on your map.
► Draw shapes for things.
► Put names with the shapes.

52   Lesson 6—Where Is "Here"?

Directions for Playing the You Are Here Game

3. Use your map to play the game. Here is how to play.
► When you hear the Go signal, move around the playground with your team.

ELABORATE   53

► When you hear the Stop signal, stop and stay in that place. It is your team's You Are Here place.

► Stand side-by-side, facing the same way.

► Look around the playground and mark where you are on your map with the arrow. Make sure the arrow is pointing the same way you are facing.

54 Lesson 6—Where Is "Here"?

► When you hear the Go signal, move around again until you hear the Stop signal.

► Then, change the position of your team's You Are Here sticky note on the map.

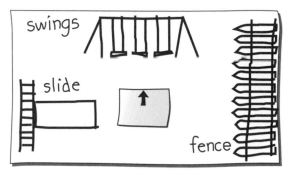

► Keep listening for Go and Stop signals. Change your marker each time you stop.

ELABORATE **55**

Assessment Strategies

So far in this lesson, you have assessed students' ability to describe position.

• Students contributed to developing a map of the classroom.

• They made a team map of the playground.

• They accurately indicated their changing position on the classroom map and on the team map of the playground.

You have assessed students' ability to connect describing position in the classroom activities to how one describes position in a real-world context.

9. Continuing Assessment

► When the class returns to the classroom, continue to assess students' developing understanding.

► Help students reflect on what they have been doing and why they have been doing it with dialogue similar to the following.

• How did we describe the position of the crayons in the *Put-It-In-Position Game?* (For example, "two steps to the front of C.Q. and one step to the left.")

• Someone could find the crayon because we described its position with words.

• How did your team show its position when we played the *You Are Here Game?* (By putting the *You Are Here* sticky note on the map)

• You can describe where something is by telling about its position with words, but you also can show something or someone's position with pictures and maps.

★ See student page 56

▶ Introduce *Checking Understanding* and explain as necessary. Direct students to answer the questions in their own science folders. Collect and review the science folders when students complete them.

▶ The following are possible statements your students may write in answer to the questions in *Checking Understanding*.

1. The sticky note showed where the team was on the playground when we stopped. The arrow showed which way we were facing.

2. We kept moving the sticky note on the map because we moved around the playground. The sticky note showed where we stopped.

3. The swings and slide did not move, but we moved. Because we moved, things were in different positions from us. One time the swings were in front of us. After we moved, the swings were in back of, or to the left of us.

Information for the Teacher

Directions for the *You Are Here Game*

• When you give the Go signal, students move around the playground with their teams.

• When you give the Stop signal, teams stop. Students in each team stand side-by-side, facing the same way.

• Teams look around the playground and mark where they are on their map with the sticky note. The sticky note shows their *You Are Here* place.

• When you give the Go signal, teams continue the sequence. @

Checking Understanding

Write about these questions in your science folder.

1. What did the sticky note on your team map mean? What did the arrow show?

2. Why did you keep moving the sticky note on your team map?

3. Every time you stopped in the game, things were in a different position from you.
   ▶ Did the swings and slide really move?
   ▶ How do you explain their "changing" positions?

56   Lesson 6—Where Is "Here"?

Picture the Position

ELABORATE/ EVALUATE

Students consider the problem of not only finding Waldo, in Where's Waldo, but describing his position relative to other objects. Then, teams look at a picture of the zany town of Norule. They locate specific objects in the picture and describe the position of the objects in relation to a variety of other objects. As teams work, each student demonstrates understanding of relative position in an individual interview with the teacher.

Estimated Time: 2 class sessions, plus additional time to interview individual students

Purpose: To continue developing students' ability to describe position from a reference object other than themselves

To allow students and the teacher to assess students' understanding of describing relative position

OUTCOMES	ASSESSMENT INDICATORS
	Students show they have achieved the outcome by:
Conceptual	
Students extend their understanding of describing position relative to other objects.	• looking at a picture and putting themselves in the position of people or objects in the picture, and • describing the position of a specific object in relation to a reference object in the picture.
Students assess their understanding of describing position relative to other objects.	demonstrating their understanding in the context of an individual interview by • describing the position of objects in relation to themselves, • describing the position of objects in relation to C.Q., the teacher, or a classmate, • describing the position of objects in a picture in relation to other objects, and • pointing out objects that fit a described relative position.
Scientific Inquiry	
Abilities Students are able to accurately describe the position of objects.	• describing the position of objects in relation to themselves, • describing the position of objects in relation to C.Q., the teacher, or a classmate, • describing the position of objects in a picture in relation to other objects, and • pointing out objects that fit a described relative position.
Collaborative	
Students ask for help and give help.	• asking their teammates for help in completing the *Picture the Position Record Page,* and • helping their teammates complete the record page by sharing their ideas.

Supplies

For the Entire Class:
- BLM 7-1, *Picture the Position Record Page*
- BLM MO-2, *Assessment Checklist,* optional
- class chart of helpful words to describe position
- chart paper or chalkboard
- marker, non-toxic or chalk
- stand-up figure of C.Q.
- 1 *Where's Waldo* book or comic strip

For Each Team of 3:
- 3 copies of BLM 7-1, *Picture the Position Record Page*
- 3 pencils

Before You Begin

▶ Review student pages for this lesson.

▶ Review *How to Assess Student Understanding of Relative Position* in *Information for the Teacher.*

▶ Schedule time over the next several days to individually interview students. Each interview will take approximately five minutes.

▶ If you intend to use BLM MO-2, *Assessment Checklist,* duplicate the appropriate number of copies so that you have enough to use for all students.

▶ Post the class chart of helpful words to describe position.

Teaching Strategies   Session 1

★ See student pages 57–59

1. Introducing the Lesson

▶ Assemble the class in the group area and introduce the lesson with *Waldo*.

- Show some illustrations in the *Where's Waldo* book or comic strip to the students and determine their familiarity with finding Waldo.

If you do not have a book or comic strip, or if students have had little or no experience with Waldo, briefly describe Waldo and the idea. Waldo is a male cartoon character who wears horn-rimmed glasses and a striped shirt. The illustrations are literally crammed full of people and objects, and the task is to find Waldo among the clutter.

- Together with the students, read pages 57–59 in the student guide.

Picture the Position

> May I have the comics after you read them, I.O.? I want to see how fast I can find Waldo in Where's Waldo.

Sometimes finding Waldo is easy, and sometimes it is hard. But,. . .

What if you had to describe Waldo's position from someone else in the picture?

What if you had to describe where someone else was from Waldo?

What if you had to give someone directions to Waldo's position?

Let's visit the town of Norule. Waldo won't be there, but take a look at the fine folks in Norule!

ELABORATE/EVALUATE   **57**

58   Lesson 7—Picture the Position

ELABORATE/EVALUATE   **59**

2. Practicing the Task

▶ Give students practice describing and recording relative position using the pictures on pages 58 and 59.

During this time, model elements of the team task as described on page 61 of the student guide. Reinforce that students should use their imagination to put themselves in the picture as the reference object. Remind students of the technique of seeing things in their mind's eye. Encourage students to turn the book around to help them in describing position from their own position as the reference object. Because students will write descriptions of position on their record pages, record their responses on the chart or board. The wording may vary, so write several responses to the same example. Emphasize effectively communicating where an object is, from the reference object.

- Where is the cat from the dog? *(in back of or behind the dog)*
- If you were the reference object, what would you be? *(the dog)*
- Where is the cat from the mouse? *(in front of the mouse)*
- If you were the reference object, what would you be? *(the mouse)*
- Where is the traffic light from the boy fishing? *(to the boy's right, or beside the boy on his right)*
- If you were the reference object, what would you be? *(the traffic light)*

- Where is the picnic from the boy fishing? *(In back of or behind the boy and to his left)*

▶ If students only respond "in back of," ask questions similar to the following to help them extend their description of position.

- Is the picnic right in back of the boy fishing?
- What else could you add to describe where the picnic is from the boy?
- Is the picnic in back of the boy and to his right?
- Where is the kite from the boy flying it?
- Is it above (higher than, over) the boy and to his left?

▶ Take as much time as necessary to help students be able to put themselves in the place of someone or something in the picture and describe other pictured objects from that point of view. If you think simulating position would be helpful, invite students to pretend they are in specific positions using brief skits or role playing.

3. Closing the Session

▶ Tell students that they will put themselves in the *Norule* picture again in the next session.

Teaching Strategies Session 2

★ See student pages 60–62

4. Describing Position

▶ Introduce the task with strategies similar to the following.

- Review the *Directions for Describing Position in Norule* in the student guide.

- Emphasize that students should ask their teammates for help, but each student should describe the positions on his/her own paper.

- Point out the class chart of helpful words from Lesson 1, and encourage students to use it to help them describe position.

▶ When teams seem to understand the task, have them begin.

Initially, circulate among students and check to be sure they are on the right track. Redirect them with questions if necessary.

▶ As teams work, interview students one at a time, using a process similar to *How to Assess Student Understanding of Relative Position* in *Information for the Teacher.*

As students come to you, have them bring their papers so you can check for any difficulties.

Describing Position In Norule

Norule is a very busy place. Many things are happening. Some things in Norule are funny.

What if you were **in** Norule?

What if you saw something funny?

What if you wanted your teammates to see it too?

How would you describe where the funny thing was?

How could you describe the position of the funny thing?

Use the pictures of the town to help you with this task.

Team Task
Put yourselves in the position of some folks and things in Norule. Talk about it with the team. Then write what you think on your own record page.

Team Skill

Ask for help and give help.

Team Jobs

Manager Tracker Messenger

60 Lesson 7—Picture the Position

Team Supplies

3 Picture the Position Record Pages

3 pencils

Directions for Describing Position in Norule

1. Read the first question from the Picture the Position Record Page with your team.

▶ Talk about it.

▶ What is the reference object in the question? (The reference object is already circled in Question 1.)

▶ Pretend **you** are the reference object.

▶ Turn the picture around if it helps you pretend to be the reference object.

▶ Then **describe where** the is from you on your own record page.

ELABORATE/EVALUATE **61**

2. In back of, or behind, the donkey.

3. To the left of the girl in the plane, and below (under). Students might not recognize that the plane is higher than the boy.

4. To the right of and above the man with the tennis racket.

5. In front of and to the left of the bank robber. Students might not recognize that the cow is "to the left" of the robber.

6. In back of (behind) and to the left of the cow.

7. Above (up) and to the right of the dog, cat, and mouse.

8. To the right of and below (under, down, lower than) the giraffe.

9. In front of and to the right of (also below, under, down, lower than) the boy in the swing.

10. In front of and to the right of the boy.

5. Sharing Descriptions

▶ After teams complete the task, assemble the students and review their record pages.

- Invite students to share their descriptions and discuss them if there is a difference other than wording.

- Continue to focus students' attention on the connection between the reference object and the described position, as you have done in previous lessons.

- Look for the following descriptions of position for each of the ten questions.

  1. In front of the captain and to the left. Students might not recognize the "in front of" because the boy is *slightly* in front of the captain.

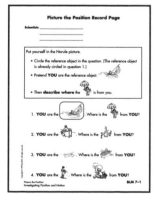

6. Continuing Assessment

▶ Collect and review students' record pages. Add them to your notes from interviews of individual students.

Information for the Teacher

How to Assess Student Understanding of Relative Position

Although time-consuming, individual interviews and performance are the most effective strategies for assessing understanding in this learning cycle. Such interviews give students an opportunity to justify their responses, and they provide you with insight into their perceptions. In addition, you have the advantage of varying the assessment to correspond with the level of each student.

In the assessment, students demonstrate their understanding of describing relative position in relation to other objects.

- Students describe the position of objects in relation to themselves.
- Students describe the position of objects in relation to C.Q., the teacher, or a classmate.
- Students describe the position of objects in a picture in relation to other objects.
- Students point out specific objects that fit a described relative position.

Structure brief tasks and simple questions. Before you begin reviewing the following sample assessments, note the following information.

- "Max" is the student being interviewed in the examples.
- Notice that the sample assessment tasks correspond with the indicators above, in difficulty and abstraction.
- Encourage students to turn themselves in the corresponding position of the reference object, and to turn the *Norule* picture around, if necessary.
- Ask questions to find out if students recognize the reference object they are using to describe the position of something.

Students describe the position of objects in relation to themselves.

1. Direct Max to stand anywhere in the classroom away from the working teams, and accompany him to that place.
2. Select several surrounding objects, one at a time, and ask Max to tell where each object is from him.
3. Direct Max to stay in the same spot, but to turn around and face the opposite direction. Then, invite him to tell where the same objects are from him.
4. Ask Max why his description of a specific object changed.

Students describe the position of objects in relation to C.Q., the teacher, or a classmate.

Select one or more of the following options.

1. Direct Max to place the stand-up figure of C.Q. somewhere in the interview area, to select objects near C.Q., and to describe the objects' positions relative to C.Q.
2. Have Max point out a specific classmate, for example, "Tia." Using Tia as a reference object, ask questions such as, "Where is _____ from Tia?"

   Direct Max to stand in different spots relative to you. You might say, "Stand in front of me and to my left."

Students describe the position of objects in a picture in relation to other objects.

Using the picture of *Norule,* ask Max questions such as the following:

- Where is the clown in the chimney from the boy in the picnic? (*in back of, behind*)
- Where is the clown from the girl in the picnic? (*in front of*)
- Where is the bird nest from the boy cooking a hot dog? (*above, or up from, and to his left*)
- Where is the baby driving the bus from the giraffe? (*in back of, or behind, and lower than, or down from*)

Students point out objects that fit a described relative position.

Relative to the specific reference objects, ask questions such as the following:

- What is something that is in front of you and to your left?
- Who is in back of Tia and *to her right?*
- What is something that is in back of me and to my right?
- In the picture of *Norule,* who is the first person to the left of the girl climbing the slide? (*the man cooking on the grill*)
- In the Norule picture, what building is to the right of the girl driving the steam roller? (*Norule Bank*) ◉

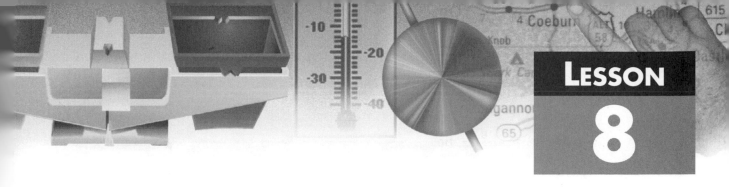

Changing Position

Students consider the changing position of their sticky notes on team playground maps in Lesson 6 and discuss what the change indicated. Then, they look for changes in sets of *Before* and *After* pictures. Students generalize that, in each set of pictures, something moved, resulting in a change in position. Students develop a class chart of ways to describe motion. Then students record ideas in their science folders about a time when they described the motion of something.

Estimated Time:
1 class session

Purpose: To assess students' current understanding of describing the motion of objects

To engage students' interest in describing the motion of objects

OUTCOMES	ASSESSMENT INDICATORS
	Students show they have achieved the outcome by:
Conceptual	
Students express their current understanding of describing the motion of objects.	• writing and drawing about a time when they described the motion of something, and • contributing to a class chart of what types of things they might describe about an object's motion.

Supplies

For the Entire Class:
- chart paper
- markers, non-toxic
- 1 team map from Lesson 6, *Where Is "Here"?*

For Each Student:
- science folder
- pencil

Before You Begin

▶ Review the pages in the student guide for this lesson.

▶ Decide which students you will assign to each team of three for this learning cycle of the module. Make a record of these assignments.

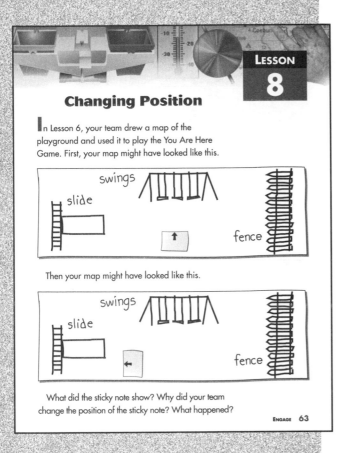

Changing Position

In Lesson 6, your team drew a map of the playground and used it to play the You Are Here Game. First, your map might have looked like this.

Then your map might have looked like this.

What did the sticky note show? Why did your team change the position of the sticky note? What happened?

ENGAGE **63**

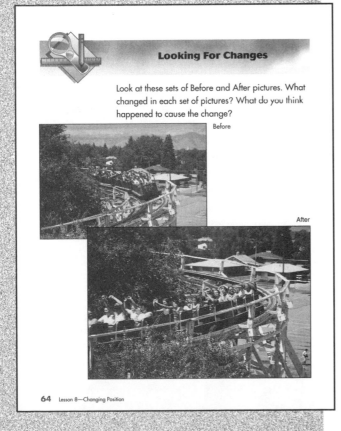

Looking For Changes

Look at these sets of Before and After pictures. What changed in each set of pictures? What do you think happened to cause the change?

Before

After

64 Lesson 8—Changing Position

Teaching Strategies   Session 1

★ See student page 63

1. Introducing the Lesson

▶ Remind the class of a specific lesson in which students changed their positions.

- Display a team's playground map from Lesson 6, *Where Is "Here"?*

- Ask students to recall what they did in the lesson to make the maps.

▶ Direct students' attention to page 63, and briefly read and discuss the pages with students.

Students should recall that the sticky note represented the position of their team at that time. When the team moved from one place to another on the playground, teammates changed the position of the sticky note to correspond with the changing position of the team.

★ See student pages 64–67

2. Looking for Changes

▶ Help students recognize that a change in position is evidence of movement (motion) with strategies similar to these.

- As a class, look at and discuss the change in each set of pictures.

Students should recognize that an object changed position in each set of pictures. They should be aware that, in order to be shown in a different position in the After photo, the object must have moved or been moved from one place to another.

- Connect students' inferences to the term **evidence**.

Students inferred that because an object changed its position, the object moved. An object's change in position from a Before *to an* After *photo is* **evidence** *that the object moved.*

Before

After

Before

After

3. Describing Ways That Things Move

▶ With students, read this section in the student guide.

▶ Invite students to brainstorm and to develop a class chart of ways people describe how objects move.

▶ Write students suggestions on the chart just as students suggest them (fast, slow, steady, round and round, straight, zigzag, back and forth, up, down, roll, slide, tumble, jerk, stop and start, spin, twirl, and so forth).

The purpose of developing a class chart at this time is to give you insight into students' current ideas about describing motion and to engage students' interest in describing motion. Students will continue to add to the chart throughout the module. Consequently, do not spend too much time on it initially.

In the first set of pictures, the roller coaster must have moved. In each of the other sets, something or someone must have moved.

▶ How do you know?

▶ What is your evidence?

Evidence is what you find out that helps you know something.

Describing Ways That Things Move

You saw a change in position in each set of pictures. You described the changes in position. But what if you saw the changes happen?

▶ How do you think the things in the pictures moved?

▶ How would you describe how those things or people moved?

▶ What are some words that describe how things move?

4. Introducing the Term Motion

★ See student page 68

▶ Ask students what people call moving from one place to another.

With students, read and discuss *A Name for Changing Position*.

*Terms such as **motion** are useful in helping primary students express their ideas. However, understanding the concept is more important than labeling it. It is perfectly acceptable for students to use the phrase "the way things move" or the term "movement" instead of motion.*

▶ After students have read and discussed the section, ask them to suggest a title for the class chart.

Students might suggest "Describing Motion," "Ways Things Move," or another appropriate title.

Assessment Strategies

At this point in the lesson, you have received an indication of how individual students currently describe the motion of objects by noting their contributions to the class chart.

5. Continuing Assessment

▶ Continue assessing students' current thinking about describing motion with the following strategies.

- Discuss the photo collage of motion on page 68.

- Ask students to think of a time they described the motion of something.

- Direct students to write and draw about such a time in their folders.

- Review students' folders to gain further insight into students' thinking.

A Name for Changing Position

When someone or something moves from one place to another place, we call it **motion**. You already know a lot about motion. In the next lessons, you will find out more about describing motion.

Now, do these things on your own.

Think of a time when you described the motion of something.

▶ Write about it.
▶ Draw a picture of it.

68   Lesson 8—Changing Position

Motion and Paths

Students listen to a story about a Scwinch who makes many yarn paths from his house to the delicious swizzle plants. On their record page, students trace imaginary paths that the Scwinch could have taken. Then, students create I.O.'s path on a ski map by matching pictures of I.O. skiing with the corresponding locations on the map.

Estimated Time:
2 class sessions

....

Purpose: To allow students to explore paths as a record of motion
To allow students to graphically record motion

....

OUTCOMES	ASSESSMENT INDICATORS
	Students show they have achieved the outcome by:
Conceptual	
Students recognize that paths are a record of motion.	• drawing multiple, imaginary paths for the Scwinch at intervals during the story,
Students recognize that they can describe an object's motion by tracing its position over time.	• matching pictures of I.O.'s changing position to the corresponding positions on an illustrated map, and • drawing I.O.'s path down the hill.
Scientific Inquiry	
Abilities Students use data to construct a reasonable explanation.	• collecting data by matching pictures of I.O.'s changing position to the corresponding positions on an illustrated map, and • using the data to draw I.O.'s path down the hill.
Collaborative	
Students ask for help and give help.	• asking for help from their teammates in completing the task, *Tracing I.O.'s Path*, and • giving their teammates help on the task when requested to do so.

Supplies

For the Entire Class:
- BLM 9-1, *The Scwinch's Paths*
- BLM 9-2, *I.O.'s Path Record Page*

For Each Student:
- 1 copy of BLM 9-1, *The Scwinch's Paths*
- 1 copy of BLM 9-2, *I.O.'s Path Record Page*
- 4 crayons, 1 pink, 1 blue, and any 2 other colors
- 1 writing board, such as a book, tray, or clipboard
- pencil

Before You Begin

▶ Review the student pages for this lesson

▶ Review the story, *The Scwinch and the Glump,* at the end of this lesson.

▶ Duplicate 1 copy of BLM 9-1, *The Scwinch's Paths* and 1 copy of BLM 9-2, *I.O.'s Path Record Page,* for each student.

Teaching Strategies   Session 1

1. Introducing the Lesson

▶ Direct students to bring to the group area four crayons (a pink, a blue, and two other colors of their choice) and a writing board of some kind.

▶ Introduce the idea of a path by asking several students to describe the path they took to get to the group area.

▶ Ask questions to probe students' thinking about the difficulty of accurately describing paths.

- Was it hard for you to remember your path?

- Was it hard to know which path your classmates took from their description of their paths?

2. Introducing The Scwinch and the Glump

▶ Introduce the story, *The Scwinch and the Glump* and read it to the class, stopping and interacting with students as indicated in the story.

- After the first stop in the story, distribute to each student 1 copy of BLM 9-1, *The Scwinch's Paths,* and invite them to draw a pink path from the Scwinch's house to the scwiz-zleberries.

- At the next stop in the story, invite students to draw a different path: a blue path from the Scwinch's house to the scwizzleberries.

- At the third stop in the story, have students use their extra crayons and draw two additional paths from the Scwinch's house to the scwizzle plants.

The students choose their own paths, but each color should show a different route.

3. Establishing a Connection Between a Path and Motion

▶ Briefly discuss the story and BLM 9-1, *The Scwinch's Paths,* by asking questions similar to these.

- How did the yarn help the Scwinch? *(The yarn made a path for the Scwinch to follow home when it was dark and he couldn't see.)*

- How did the Scwinch use the yarn to make a path? *(The Scwinch unrolled the ball of yarn behind him to make a path.)*

- What does a path do or show? *(A path shows where something or someone went.)*

A path traces motion. Students might mention dirt trails through the woods as paths. Help them realize that paths such as established trails still trace the motion of people or animals.

- When you compare your paper to the paper of someone around you, are the paths exactly the same? If not, are some paths "right" and other paths "wrong"? *(Paths differ from student to student. All paths are right as long as they lead from the Scwinch's house to the scwizzle plants.)*

- How many paths from the Scwinch's house to the scwizzle plants are possible? Why do you think so? *(Many, many paths are possible. Every time the Scwinch goes a different way, even if it is only a little different, like going all the way around a tree rather than by it, he makes a new path.)*

4. Reinforcing Visual Spatial Skills

▶ Ask students if the story told which paths the Scwinch really took. If the story didn't tell which paths, how were they able to draw the paths on their paper?

Students will likely agree that they didn't actually know which paths the Scwinch took, so they drew imaginary paths.

► Probe students' understanding of "imaginary."

Students might describe imaginary as not real, something made up in someone's mind.

► Explain that, since the story gave no clues about the paths the Scwinch took, students had to "see" the paths in their minds, or with their "mind's eye."

► Inform the students that, in the next session, I.O. will give clues so that they can trace her path, but they will still "see her path with their mind's eye."

► If you have time, suggest that students draw on the back of their paper an imaginary picture showing how the Scwinch and Glump might look.

★ See student pages 69–75

Teaching Strategies   Session 2

5. Tracing I.O.'s Path

► Introduce the activity, *Tracing I.O.'s Path*, in the student guide and review the directions as necessary.

► Emphasize that, although they will help one another, teammates will fill in their own record page.

► Assign students to their same teams and workstations and have them begin the task. As students work, circulate and observe the following.

• Are teammates helping one another by discussing I.O.'s route before they mark their maps?

• Do students realize that they should put on the map symbols of the corresponding pictures?

• When teams share their record pages, do they notice and discuss differences in the paths?

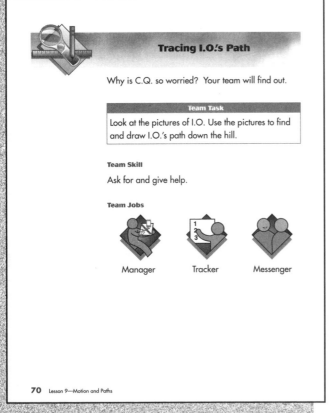

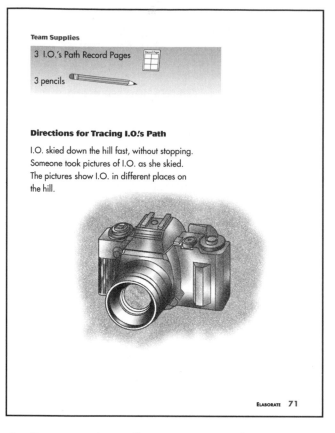

Team Supplies

3 I.O.'s Path Record Pages

3 pencils

Directions for Tracing I.O.'s Path

I.O. skied down the hill fast, without stopping. Someone took pictures of I.O. as she skied. The pictures show I.O. in different places on the hill.

ELABORATE **71**

1. Look at the pictures. They are all mixed up.

72 Lesson 9—Motion and Paths

6. Processing the Team Task

▶ After students finish, discuss the task with the class.

- Compare some of the record pages and invite students to identify differences between them.

- Encourage student-to-student interaction by inviting students to directly question other students about their paths. Encourage students to justify their paths.

- Help students realize that, as long as the sequence of symbols is the same, paths can vary somewhat and still be correct.

ELABORATE **73**

2. Look at the map of the hill on your record page.

3. Use the pictures and the map to find I.O.'s path. Do these things.
   ▶ One at a time, match each picture to a place on the hill.
   ▶ When you find a match look at the mark on the picture.
   ▶ Draw the mark on the same position on the map.

▶ Match all of the pictures and mark them on the map.

4. Connect all the marks to show I.O.'s path down the hill.
   ▶ Make your path look like I.O.'s ski tracks.
   ▶ What does a ski path look like?
   ▶ See I.O.'s hints.

74 Lesson 9—Motion and Paths

My path is straight in some places, but it is curvy, too. When I don't want to go too fast on the steep places, I wind back and forth across the hill.

5. When all teammates finish their paths, meet with another team.
   ▶ Compare your paths. Are they different?
   ▶ Talk about it.
   ▶ If you get evidence that makes you change your mind, change your path.

6. Be ready to talk about I.O.'s path with the class.

ELABORATE 75

Assessment Strategies

At this point in the lesson, you have assessed students understanding of describing motion in these ways.

- You observed students draw the Scwinch's imaginary paths on their record pages and heard them express what those paths represented.

- You observed and interacted with students as they traced I.O.'s path down the hill.

- You listened as students discussed and justified their record of I.O.'s path.

7. Continuing Assessment

▶ Determine if students connect both the Scwinch's and I.O.'s paths to the concept of motion by discussing questions such as these.

Students will respond with their own ideas. Encourage them to justify their responses and to ask for justification from others. It is unlikely that students' responses will match the samples below. Use the sample responses to help you in the discussion.

- What does I.O.'s path do or show? *(I.O.'s path shows where she went; it traces I.O.'s motion down the hill. The path makes a record of I.O. as she moves from one position to another.)*

- Is there more than one path that I could take down the hill? Why do you think so? *(Yes. There is not just one set path. Just like the Scwinch, I.O. chose her own path. She could ski down other ways since she was choosing her path.)*

- Do you think that the Scwinch would have more paths to and from the scwizzle-berries, than I.O. would have down the hill? Why do you think so? *(I.O. might not have as many paths as the Scwinch because it might be too rocky or steep for her in some places. The land between the Scwinch's house and the scwizzle plants seemed to be flat, so he could go many ways.)*

★ See student page 76

Continue assessing students' developing understanding by assigning and reviewing *Checking Understanding* in the student guide.

Lesson Extensions

Language Arts, Physical Education: Have students dramatize the story, *The Scwinch and the Glump.* Choose classroom objects to represent the Scwinch's house and the scwizzle plants. The class can spread out to represent the forest. Have students take turns playing the parts of the Scwinch and the Glump. Emphasize the decisions the Scwinch and the Glump make to solve problems.

Science: Lead the students to a special class leaving a yarn path behind you as you go. While students are in the special class, use a different color of yarn to make another, unfamiliar path back to the classroom. When students are ready to return to the classroom, ask them where both paths lead. Students should know that the first path leads back to the classroom, but they will not know the destination of the second path. Lead students along the second path. After students return to the classroom, challenge them to help design other routes to the same location.

Science: Take the class on a walk around the school grounds and search for paths. Common paths include hallways, sidewalks, dirt paths, driveways, and roadways. In some locations, students might find a set of animal tracks.

Art, Science: Have students tip and rotate shallow boxes or pie pans containing one or two marbles. Challenge students to describe the paths of the marbles. Then, have students record the path by placing a sheet of plain paper in the box or pan and dipping the marble into tempera paint before students tip and rotate the container a second time.

Checking Understanding

Do these things on your own.

1. Think of a time when you went from one place to another.
   ► Did you make your own path?
   ► Draw and write about it in your science folder.
2. Think about how your team worked together.
   ► How did you help your teammates?
   ► How did your teammates help you?
   ► Write about it in your science folder.

Information for the Teacher

The Scwinch and the Glump*

Once there were two strange creatures. One was the Scwinch and the other was the Glump.

The Glump was a huge ugly creature. The Scwinch was a friendly little fellow who had a small body and a big brain. Now the Glump was mad at the Scwinch because the Scwinch always outsmarted him.

"He always tricks me," the poor Glump said to himself. "If I ever catch him, I'm going to do something terrible to him. I will make him eat lots and lots of my homemade wartichoke pie because it's the only food he can't stand." And that nasty old Glump chuckled to himself, "Chuckle, chuckle, chuckle."

Meanwhile, the Scwinch got a letter from his Aunt Artesia. It said:

Dear Nephew Scwinch,

I am sending you a map that shows how to get to the place where the most delicious scwizzle plants grow. Their berries are simply delightful to eat. Memorize where the path goes and destroy the map so no one else will discover the secret.

Good luck, Nephew Dear,
Your Aunt Artesia

The Scwinch studied the map carefully for a moment and then gobbled it up.

The next day he was ready to set out to find the scwizzle plants. He said to himself, "It will probably take me all day to get to the scwizzle plants. By the time I've picked a sackful of berries, it will be dark and I will get lost. How can I find my way back in the dark?"

Just then the Scwinch remembered an old ball of pink yarn he had left over from knitting himself a scarf. "If I could unroll the yarn as I go along, then I can follow it in the dark and find my way back," he chirped. And he did just that. On the way to the scwizzle plants, the Scwinch unrolled the ball of pink yarn as he went.

(Stop. Distribute 1 copy of BLM 9-1, *The Scwinch's Paths*, to each student. Invite students to draw a pink path from the Scwinch's house to the scwizzleberries.)

When the Scwinch got to the yummy scwizzle plants, he picked a whole sackful of berries. Of course, by the time he finished it was dark, so he followed his pink yarn all the way home, bending over so he could see it.

All this time the Glump had been trying to think of a way to catch the Scwinch. He was walking around in the forest thinking when he tripped over the Scwinch's pink yarn. "What's this thing?" roared the Glump. "It looks like the Scwinch's pink yarn. Why is it here? Maybe if I wait here the Scwinch will come and I can catch him!" So he stood behind a tree and waited . . . and waited . . . and waited. It was dark, and the Scwinch was on his way home. He got close to the place where the Glump was hiding. He got closer and closer and closer.

Just as the Glump was about to jump out from behind the tree, he sneezed, "Kachooie," because having his face in the tree made his nose tickle.

Immediately the Scwinch recognized that sneeze and ran as fast as he could along his little pink path until he got home safely. "Whew!" he panted. "That was a close call. That nasty Glump almost got me. He would have made me eat some of his horrible wartichoke pie if he caught me. But now I can't go along the pink path anymore because he'll be waiting there to catch me. Now what can I do?"

Suddenly the Scwinch remembered a ball of blue yarn that he had left over from knitting himself a blue toe-warmer. "I'll go a different way to the scwizzle plants and leave a path of blue yarn so I can find my way back. The Glump will still be waiting at the pink path and he'll miss me!"

(Stop. Invite students to draw a different path from the Scwinch's house to the scwizzleberries with the blue crayon.)

His idea worked just find until the Glump found the blue path and waited for the Scwinch. He would have caught him, too, but the Scwinch ran when he saw the Glump's feet sticking out from behind a tree. From then on the Scwinch went a different way each day. He used different yarn to mark each new path. The poor Glump could never catch up to the Scwinch because he was always one path behind.

(Stop. Invite students to draw, with their extra crayons, 2 different paths from the Scwinch's house to the scwizzleberries.)

Finally, the Glump decided that the only way he could catch the Scwinch would be to follow one of the paths to the scwizzle plants and hide there. So he started following a path. Fortunately, the Scwinch saw him and thought of a good way to stop him for a long time. He ran ahead and attached another ball of yarn

to the yarn that the Glump was following. Then he called to a bird he saw flying south, "Would you do me a favor? Take this ball of yarn and let it unroll behind you as you fly."

The bird said, "Certainly," and flew away.

You can guess what happened next. The poor Glump kept following and following the path until he ended up so far south that he didn't know where he was.

Since it was a nice place (wherever it was), the Glump decided to stay there and was very happy. And the Scwinch was happy too. He could eat all the scwizzleberries he wanted and not worry about getting caught and having to eat wartichoke pie. And he could take a different path every day because he had so many. ◉

*Reprinted from *Developing Mathematical Processes, Teacher's Guide, Topic 6: Movement & Direction,* The Wisconsin Research and Development Center for Cognitive Learning, University of Wisconsin-Madison.

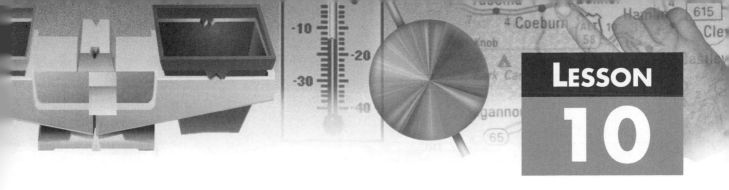

How Did It Move?

Students consider that paths of moving objects are invisible. Then teams do five investigations in which they observe and record the motion of a rubber ball. Afterward, each team makes a poster of one of the investigations and shares it with the class.

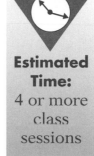

Estimated Time:
4 or more class sessions

Purpose: To allow students to describe a variety of motions
To allow students to graphically record motion

OUTCOMES	ASSESSMENT INDICATORS
	Students show they have achieved the outcome by:
Conceptual	
Students understand that, by tracing its position over time, they can describe an object's motion.	• observing and describing the motion of a rubber ball in a variety of investigations.
Students understand that objects move in many different ways.	• observing a rubber ball as it moves in a variety of ways, • describing the variety of motions with descriptors such as straight, zigzag, round and round, back and forth, and fast and slow, and • identifying other objects' motions that are specifically similar to those of the rubber ball.
Scientific Inquiry	
Abilities Students are able to accurately describe the motion of objects.	• drawing the path of a ball's motion, • writing a description of the ball's motion, and • identifying an object that has a motion similar to that of the ball.
Collaborative	
Students speak softly.	• developing criteria for "speaking softly," • monitoring the loudness of their team's conversation according to the criteria, and • assessing their success.

Supplies

For the Entire Class:
- BLM 10-1, *Describing Motion Record Page*
- 5 shallow box lids, such as the tops of boxes of copy paper
- 5 round, smooth plastic bowls, approximately 15 x 30 cm
- metric tape measure
- masking tape
- chart paper
- markers, non-toxic
- writing or drawing paper
- 10+ sheets of construction paper, 12" x 18" or larger, light-colored

For Each Team of 3:
- 1 small rubber ball
- 1 length of string, approximately 30 cm
- 1 pair of scissors
- masking tape
- 1 metric tape
- 1 copy of BLM 10-1, *Describing Motion Record Page*
- pencils

For Each Student:
- science folder
- pencil

Before You Begin

▶ Review the student pages for this lesson.

▶ Duplicate 1 copy (5 copies, optional) of BLM 10-1, *Describing Motion Record Page* for each team of 3 students. (*Note:* In Session 3, teams will record their observations of a ball's motion in 5 investigations. The student pages assume that each team will have 1 copy of the record page for the first investigation. Then, using the page as a guide, teams will write each of the names of the remaining 4 investigations on a separate sheet of paper, and record their observations beside the corresponding number. You have the option of duplicating 5 copies of BLM 10-1 for each team.)

▶ Prepare 1 or 2 sample record pages by enlarging BLM 10-1, *Describing Motion Record Page* on chart paper.

▶ Consider options in scheduling and organizing this lesson. The lesson is presented as if all teams were doing the investigations at the same time. If this is the case, you will need approximately four sessions to complete this lesson. After the first session, revise your timetable as necessary.

Teaching Strategies   Session 1

★ See student page 77

1. Introducing the Lesson

▶ Together, read and discuss page 77 in the student guide.

- As a part of the discussion, point out that if they described I.O.'s skating path to a teammate, the teammate should be able to "see" I.O.'s path with their "mind's eye."

- Discuss the idea that describing the motion of an object to someone who did not see the motion requires clear descriptions.

2. Modeling the Team Task

▶ In the group area, model the team task with 1 or 2 of the following investigations.

▶ After each investigation, fill in the charts representing the sample record pages.

How Did It Move?

In the last lesson, I.O.'s path was a record of her motion. I.O. left her path in the snow. You traced her path on your record page. Suppose you really did observe I.O. skiing. Could you describe I.O.'s path down the hill to someone else?

Suppose it was summer and you observed I.O. skate down the hill.

▶ Would I.O. leave a path like her path in the snow?

▶ Do you think you could draw I.O.'s path?

▶ Could you describe I.O.'s skating path?

▶ Could you describe I.O.'s motion?

EXPLAIN/ELABORATE **77**

DIRECTIONS FOR THE INVESTIGATIONS

Ball Drop	Ball Throw
1. Stand up and hold the ball to the front, higher than your head. 2. Choose a catcher to hold his/her hands close to the floor. 3. Drop the ball and let the catcher catch it near the floor. 4. If the catcher misses, repeat. 5. Change the distance the ball moves by having a catcher stand up and catch the ball as you drop it from the same position. Use student's responses to help you fill in the record page on chart paper. (See the illustrated samples on page 117.)	1. Stand up and gently throw the ball straight up. 2. Catch the ball with your hands in about the same position as the position from which you threw it. 3. Change the distance the ball moves by squatting down or bending over to catch the ball.

Describing Motion Record Page

Scientists _____

Investigation _____ Ball Throw _____

1. Draw the ball's path and direction.

2. Describe the ball's motion.
   The ball went up a little way. Then it came back down almost the same path as it went up. The ball went up as fast as it came down.

3. Tell or draw something else that moves like this.
   Water from a hose when you hold it straight up.

4. Change the ball's motion in some way. Describe how you changed it.
   The thrower caught the ball lower, so the ball came down farther than it went up. Like this.

Describing Motion Record Page

Scientists _____

Investigation _____ Ball Drop _____

1. Draw the ball's path and direction.

2. Describe the ball's motion.
   The ball fell straight down. It did not go real fast or real slow. The ball went from your hand to the hands near the floor.

3. Tell or draw something else that moves like this.
   Raindrops, when it is not windy.

4. Change the ball's motion in some way. Describe how you changed it.
   The catcher got the ball before it reached the floor, so the ball did not go as far.

★ See student pages 78–83

Describing Motion

I.O.'s skating path was invisible. Most moving objects leave an invisible path. But, you can observe someone or something making an invisible path.

Closely observing an object's motion is important. But clearly describing an object's motion is just as important. Your team will find out how well you can do both.

Team Task
Observe the motion of objects and describe how they move.

Team Skill

Speak softly.

Team Jobs

Manager   Tracker   Messenger

---

3. Describing Motion – Team Task

▶ Review the team task with the class, demonstrating as necessary.

▶ Invite students to establish criteria for an acceptable noise level and techniques they might use for monitoring.

▶ When teams seem to understand the task, directions, and parameters, have them begin.

▶ As teams work, do these things.

• Encourage students to talk about the ball's motion with their teammates and decide on clear descriptions before filling in their team record page.

  If teams need more space, have them write on the back of their record pages.

Team Supplies

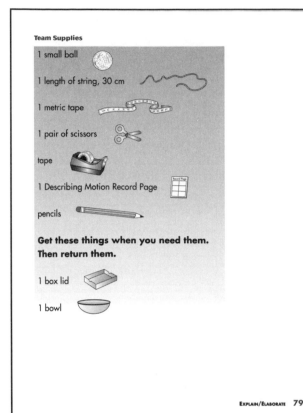

1 small ball

1 length of string, 30 cm

1 metric tape

1 pair of scissors

tape

1 Describing Motion Record Page

pencils

Get these things when you need them. Then return them.

1 box lid

1 bowl

EXPLAIN/ELABORATE   79

Directions for Describing Motion

1. Do the five investigations, one at a time. Do them in any order.

2. After each investigation, record your findings on your team's record page.

3. After you finish, be ready to share your descriptions with the class.

Ball in a Box

▶ Put the ball in a box lid.

▶ Quickly move the box from side to side, over and over again. Take turns.

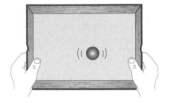

▶ Return the box lid.

80   Lesson 10—How Did It Move?

Ball in a Bowl

▶ Put the ball in a bowl.

▶ Quickly move the bowl as if it was sitting on a moving merry-go-round. Take turns.

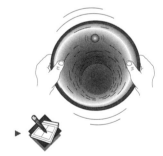

▶ Return the bowl.

Ball Toss

▶ Teammates, **A, B,** and **C,** stand like this.

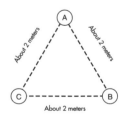

About 2 meters

EXPLAIN/ELABORATE   81

- Briefly review each team's record pages at intervals to assess the thoughtfulness and thoroughness of students' responses.

- Ask questions designed to encourage students to observe carefully and to describe their observations more accurately.

  - Tell me about the speed of the ball. Did it go as fast the whole time and then just stop?

  - Tell me more about how the ball bounced. Did it bounce just as high every time? What did the ball do after it stopped bouncing?

  - How does your drawing show which direction the ball was going?

  - What makes you think that the ball moves like a _____? What else moves like that?

  - Can you think of any other ways to change the ball's motion?

- ► **A** and **B** toss the ball back and forth to each other, using an underhand motion.
- ► **C** observes the path of the ball.
- ► Trade places so that everyone has a turn to observe the ball's path.

Ball Bounce

- ► Teammate **A** drops the ball to the floor.
- ► Teammates **B** and **C** observe the ball's path from the floor to a roll or stop.
- ► Trade places so that everyone has a turn to drop the ball.

Ball on a String

- ► Tape the string to the ball.
- ► Tape the other end of the string to the edge of the desk or table.

- ► Pull the ball to the side and let it go.

- ► Observe the ball's path.

- • Continue to refer students back to their criteria for an acceptable noise level and to their suggestions for monitoring it.
- • Continue using class time to work until all teams have completed the investigations and recorded their observations.

★ See student page 84

4. Introducing the Poster-Making Task

► Invite teams to share the results of their investigations with the class. Then, introduce *Checking Understanding*.

► Have each team choose 3 investigations of which they would like to make a team-sharing poster.

- • Assign each team one of their choices.
- • Be sure to assign each of the 5 investigations.

- ► If you have time, do this.
  - ► Let the ball go from different distances. Does the ball go faster?
  - ► Change the length of the string and let the ball go. Does it go faster?

Checking Understanding

As a team, you will make a poster of **one** investigation and share your findings with the class.

▶ Explain the directions for the poster as follows.

- Posters should represent all of the information on the *Describing Motion Record Page*. However, teams should not merely reproduce the record page for their investigation. Teams should draw on their poster and include some words.

- All teammates must help in creating the poster and in presenting it to the class.

- Emphasize to the students that, from a team's poster and presentation, someone who did not observe the ball should be able to see the ball's motion in their mind's eye.

- After a team presents its poster, the class will decide how clearly the poster and presentation described the ball's motion.

Assessment Strategies

Throughout this lesson you have had multiple opportunities to observe and to interact with students as they investigated and described the motion of a rubber ball. In addition, periodically reviewing each team's record page has helped you assess students' developing understanding of describing motion.

5. Continuing Assessment

▶ When teams complete their posters, invite the class to develop a system for judging the posters before teams present them. For example, students could develop a system such as this one.

- Hold up 1 finger if students felt they could clearly "see" the ball's motion in their mind's eye.

- Hold up 2 fingers if they could "see" some of the ball's motion but the team's poster or presentation was incomplete.

- Hold up 3 fingers if students were not able to "see" the ball's motion at all after the presentation.

▶ Have each team briefly share its poster with the class.

▶ Encourage students to interact directly with the presenting team.

▶ After a team's presentation, have the class use the system they developed to assess the effectiveness of the team's presentation.

▶ Have teams display their posters in the classroom or in a common area of the school.

▶ Collect and review the record pages.

Drop Races

**ELABORATE/
EVALUATE**

**Estimated
Time:**
3 class
sessions

Teams race drops of liquid starch and water down a ramp and determine the faster and slower of the two drops. Then teams create a mixture of the starch and water from their own formula and race drops of the three liquids. Students consider the relationship between the set distance from start to finish and the time the drops took to finish the race. Then they use their ideas to justify describing one drop's motion as "fastest" or "slowest." Students show what they know about describing motion by changing the direction and speed of drops and describing the resulting changes in motion.

Purpose: To allow students to describe the speed of objects

To assess students' understanding, in a new context, of how the motion of objects can be described

OUTCOMES	ASSESSMENT INDICATORS
	Students show they have achieved the outcome by:
Conceptual	
Students recognize that they can describe an object's motion by measuring its position over time.	• racing drops of liquid from start to finish down a ramp, • expressing that fast drops moved the same set distance in less time and slow drops in more time, and • mixing a drop that was neither the fastest nor the slowest in a race.
Students assess their understanding of how the motion of objects can be described.	• mixing a drop that was neither the fastest nor the slowest of three drops and describing the motion of the drop appropriately, • changing the direction of a drop, and describing the resulting change in motion appropriately.
Scientific Inquiry	
Abilities Students are able to accurately describe the motion of objects.	• describing the speed of the drops as slowest, fastest, and between the fastest and slowest, and • justifying their descriptions.
Students become aware of the difference between a guess and a prediction.	• guessing which of two drops will be faster, • testing the drops individually, and • using the results of the tests to predict which drop will be faster.
Collaborative	
Teams share and take turns.	• sharing ideas about a formula for the green drops, • sharing ideas about how to change the speed and directions of the drops, and • taking turns testing their ideas.

Supplies

For the Entire Class:	For Each Team of 3
• BLM 11-1, *Drop Races Record Page*	• 1 tray
• 1 container of liquid laundry starch	• 3 dropper bottles
• 1 measuring cup, 500 milliliters	• 1 Drop Race board
• 1 funnel	• paper towels
• food coloring, 1 small bottle each of blue and yellow	• 1 copy of BLM 11-1, *Drop Races Record Page*
• water	• pencils

Before You Begin

▶ Review the student pages for this lesson.

▶ Review the following sections in *Information for the Teacher.*

  • *Guidelines on Guesses and Predictions*

  • *Reflections on How Could You Find Out?*

▶ Duplicate one copy of BLM 11-1, *Drop Races Record Page,* for each team.

▶ Prepare the dropper bottles for the teams. Each team will need 3 dropper bottles—one with blue liquid, one with yellow, and one empty.

  • To prepare the blue liquid, pour 300 milliliters of liquid starch into the measuring cup and add several drops of blue food coloring. Stir well. Using the funnel, add a small amount of blue liquid to one dropper bottle for each team.

  • To prepare the yellow liquid, pour 500 milliliters of water into the measuring cup and add several drops of yellow food coloring. Use the funnel to pour a small amount of yellow liquid into one dropper bottle for each team.

▶ Since you will be using food coloring, you may want students to wear paint shirts during this lesson to protect their clothing.

▶ Review the *Lesson Extensions* to determine if you want students to leave the liquid in the dropper bottles in Strategy 5, or dump it out and rinse the bottles.

Drop Races

In Lesson 10, the little ball bounced up and down. It swirled around and around, and zigzagged back and forth. You discovered a lot about the motion of the rubber ball. What can you discover about the motion of drops?

Do you ever go on a rainy day walk with a friend?

Walking in the rain is nice if the raindrops are soft and warm.

But raindrops are not always soft and warm.

Sometimes thunder booms, lightning flashes, and the wind blows the rain against the window.

ELABORATE/EVALUATE **85**

What do you do on those stormy days when you must stay inside? Do you ever watch the raindrops fall on the window? The motion of raindrops is fun to watch.

► Some drops hit the window and roll straight down.

► Some drops stay in one place for a long, long time. Then all of a sudden they race down the window!

Do you ever wonder which drop will win the race to the bottom of the window?

86 Lesson 11—Drop Races

★ See student pages 85–90

Teaching Strategies   Session 1

1. Introducing the Lesson

► Together with students, read and discuss pages 85-90 in the student guide.

► Prepare students for the first activity, *Finding the Faster Drop.*

• Review the directions as necessary.

• Assign teams to workstations and have them begin.

► As teams work, take notes on their comments, questions, and conversations.

Finding the Faster Drop

Your team can watch a drop race even if it is not raining.

The drops in this race are more colorful than raindrops.

Team Task
Race the blue and the yellow drops.
Find out which drop is **faster**. Tell why you think so.

Team Skills

Share and take turns.

Team Jobs

Manager   Tracker   Messenger

ELABORATE/EVALUATE **87**

---

2. Thinking about Guesses and Predictions

▶ When teams finish, assemble them in the large group area with their record pages.

▶ Review Questions 1 and 2 on the record page by asking questions such as these.

The purpose of these two questions and testing the drops one at a time is to help students become aware of the difference between a guess and prediction. See Information for the Teacher *for additional information.*

Team Supplies

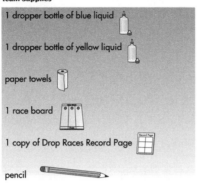

1 dropper bottle of blue liquid

1 dropper bottle of yellow liquid

paper towels

1 race board

1 copy of Drop Races Record Page

pencil

Directions for Finding the Faster Drop

1. Guess whether the blue or yellow drop will be faster.
   ▶ Write your team's **guess** on the record page.
2. Predict whether the blue or yellow drop will be faster by doing these things.
   ▶ Test the drops, one color at a time, like this.

Don't race the drops together yet.

▶ Decide which color was faster.
▶ Write what your team **predicts** on the record page.
▶ Write why you think so.

3. Get ready to race the drops.
   Choose 1 Starter and 2 Judges.
   ▶ Put the race board flat on the floor or table.
   ▶ Put a blue drop in one circle.
   ▶ Put a yellow drop in another circle.

Don't worry. Everyone will have a turn to do every job.

---

4. Now race the drops.
   The Starter will do these things.
   ▶ Lift up the end of the race board just high enough for the drops to roll.
   ▶ Hold the board still until the drops cross the finish line.
   ▶ After the race, dry the race board.

The Judges will do these things.
   ▶ Watch the race closely.
   ▶ Decide which drop was faster.
   ▶ Fill in your record page for Race 1.

5. Race the drops two more times.
6. Which drop is faster? How do you know?
   ▶ Talk about it.
   ▶ On your record page, write how you know.

Change jobs for each race.

- Which drop did you **guess** would be the faster of the two drops? Why did you think so?

  Students should not have any data to support their guess.

- What did you do before you predicted which drop would win?

  Students should remember that they tested the drops one at a time, and then recorded their prediction.

- Why do you think you tested the drops one at a time before you predicted which drop would win?

  Students might or might not realize that testing the drops individually helped them predict rather than guess.

- Which drop did you **predict** would win? Why did you choose that drop? How did your test help you predict which drop would win?

  Students might realize that testing the drops one at a time gave them more information on which to make a prediction.

- Was your guess the same as your prediction? If not, why not?

3. Describing the Speed of Two Drops

▶ Point out that teams have been racing the drops and ask students to explain a "race."

▶ Focus students' attention on Questions 3 and 4 on their record page.

- Which drop was faster? How could you tell?

Students should agree that the yellow drop always finished first, unless it fell off the side of the ramp. Students might respond that they knew the yellow drop was faster for these reasons.

"It beat the blue drops."

"It crossed the finish line before the blue drop."

"It got to the finish line first or faster."

- Which drop went farther?

  Students should realize that both drops went the same distance because both drops raced from the starting line to the finish line. However, students might not have waited for the blue drop to complete the race.

- Which drop covered the distance in less time?

  Students should realize that the yellow drop finished in less time. Students might also realize that it took the blue drop more time to cover the same distance.

- One of the drops moved faster than the other. How would you explain to someone what it means to be "faster"?

5. Closing the Session

▶ Tell students that they will race more drops in the next session.

▶ Collect teams' record pages and tell students where to store the supplies.

Find the Fastest Drop

Now your team will race a blue drop, a yellow drop, and a green drop. You will mix some of the blue and yellow liquids to make a green liquid. Will the green drop be speedy or slow?

Team Task

Make green liquid.
Race the blue, yellow, and green drops.
Find out which drop is **fastest**.

Team Skill

Share and take turns.

Team Jobs

Manager

Tracker

Messenger

ELABORATE/EVALUATE 91

Team Supplies

1 dropper bottle of blue liquid

1 dropper bottle of yellow liquid

1 empty dropper bottle

paper towels

1 race board

your team's Drop Races Record Page

pencil

Directions for Finding the Fastest Drop

1. First, make green drops by doing these things.
   ▶ Decide how many blue drops and how many yellow drops you want to mix.
   ▶ Write your team's **formula** on the record page.

Teaching Strategies   Session 2

★ See student pages 91–93

6. Introducing *Finding the Fastest Drop*

▶ With students, read and discuss the activity as necessary.

▶ Direct the same teams to their workstations and have them begin.

▶ Interact with students as they work.

  • Check each team's written formula and ask students for an explanation.

  • Listen to team discussions to gain insight into students' reasoning concerning their predictions.

  • As you talk to teams, encourage less verbal students to share their ideas.

▶ When all teams complete the task and record page, direct students to do these things.

▶ Put the blue and yellow drops in the empty dropper bottle.
▶ Put the lid on the bottle and shake it.

2. Will the green drop be speedy or slow? Predict it on your record page.

3. Race the 3 drops the same way you raced the 2 drops.

Race 3 times.
Fill in the record page after each race.
Change jobs for each race.

ELABORATE/EVALUATE 93

- Clean up their stations.
- Discuss *How Could You Find Out?* with their teams.

7. Comparing Results

▶ Assemble the teams with their record pages and process the activity by doing these things.

- Ask students to explain why their answer to Question 6 was a prediction rather than a guess.

  Students' responses should help you gain additional insight into their critical thinking skills.

- Have teams briefly share their formulas and compare race results.

8. Recording Ideas

▶ On the board, write these questions.

- Which drop was fastest?
- Why do you think so?

▶ Invite students to show what they know by writing about the questions in their science folder.

▶ After students finish, collect and review their folders. Students folders will probably include responses similar to these.

- The yellow drop was the fastest because it beat the blue and green drops.
- It crossed the finish line before the blue or green drop.
- It got to the finish line first or fastest.

Assessment Strategies

The structure of this lesson provided you with ample opportunity to observe and interact with students as they investigated and described the speed of drops of liquids.

- Students compared the motion of the drops and described each liquid as being either the fastest, slowest, or in-between.
- Students justified their descriptions on their record pages, in their science folders, and verbally.

How Could You Find Out

1. Could you change the formula to make the green drop go slower than it did? Faster?

2. If you use only the blue and yellow drops, could you make a green drop that was the fastest? Slowest?

Show What You Know

You have learned a lot about motion and how to describe it. Show what you know about motion by doing these things with your team.

1. Find a way to make a drop change direction.
2. Find a way to make a drop change speed.
   ▶ First, talk about it.
   ▶ Next, try your ideas.
   ▶ Then, write about it in your science folder.

94   Lesson 11—Drop Races

★ See student page 94

Teaching Strategies   Session 3

9. Continuing Assessment

▶ Introduce *Show What You Know* in the student guide.

▶ Explain that there are three parts to the task.

- Students need to find out how to change the motion of a drop.
- Students need to describe in their science folders how to change the motion of drops.
- Students need to work together as a team with no written directions.

▶ Explain the task as necessary and have teams begin.

Give students enough information to allow them to succeed, but not enough to undermine the open-endedness of this performance assessment.

▶ Use guidelines such as these to assess students.

- Accept any solutions to the challenges that accomplish the changes in motion. Students will probably come up with creative solutions.

- Consider the abilities of individual students as you review their science folders.

- Observe the collaborative skills of teams in problem-solving, as well as in working together.

  Your observations should provide insight into students' abilities to create their own structure, based upon their team work in previous lessons.

Lesson Extensions

Schedule time for teams to race their green drops and arrange all team bottles of green liquid in order from slowest to fastest. Challenge the class to come up with a procedure for such a race. How would students determine rank? Compare the formula of each bottle to the rank order.

Set up a center so that students can race drops of other nontoxic liquids, such as cooking oils, syrup, skim milk, 1% milk, 2% milk, whole milk, half and half, water with detergent added, and so forth.

Information for the Teacher

··

Guidelines on Guesses and Predictions

Predictions of future events are based on data or direct experience; guesses are not.

Predictions are not always correct, but they are usually good estimates. In this lesson, primary students become aware of guesses and predictions and the difference

between the two. Students' developing awareness of predictions should support interest in questions such as these.

- How do you know?

- What makes you think so?

- What evidence do you have?

Students will have multiple experiences with guesses and predictions in years to come. @

Reflections on *How Could You Find Out?*

1. To make the green drop go slower, add more blue drops. Adding more yellow drops will make the green drop faster.

2. Students may intuitively understand that the response to this question is "no", even if they can't explain it. If you used only the blue and yellow drops, you could not make a green drop that was the fastest or slowest of the three drops because if you added either blue (or green) drops to the yellow, it would slow the resulting green drop. If you added yellow (or green) to the blue, it would make the resulting green drop slower. @

Notes for Assessing Understanding and Ability

Student's Name	Conceptual Understanding	Scientific Inquiry	Ability & Understanding	Collaborative Ability

Assessment Checklist

Use this checklist to record your assessment of each student's understanding of the module outcomes. Duplicate as many copies as you need for your class.

NAME	Understands that an object's position can be described by locating it relative to other objects.	Understands that an object's motion can be described by tracing its position over time.	Understands that objects move in many different ways.	Understands that an object's motion can be described by measuring its position over time.	Shows basic skills for working in collaborative teams.	Asks for and gives help in his or her collaborative team.

Module Overview
Investigating Position and Motion

BLM MO–2

Sample Letter to Parents and Guardians

Dear Parent or Guardian:

From the time they are born, the primary job of children is to find out about the world around them. That also is the job of science—to find out how the world works. The purpose of science in elementary school is to bring children and science together in a meaningful way so children do not lose their sense of wonder and curiosity as they develop a better understanding of the world.

Your child's world is full of engaging objects to investigate and to think and talk about. Each of these objects takes up space and occupies a position. Many objects can change position as a result of motion. Children constantly observe these spatial relationships and express their ideas in everyday language.

I couldn't catch the ball because it was way over my head.

When I wound up in the swing, I spun around really fast. Then I went slower and slower until the swing finally stopped.

This science module provides opportunities for your child to investigate spatial concepts. Describing the position and motion of objects requires visualization and spatial thinking ability—the ability to visualize and manipulate images in the mind's eye. Visualization/spatial skills are crucial in helping children understand how their world (and beyond) works. Your child's simple experiences in this module provide the foundation for future understanding of complex concepts such as the movement of the earth around the sun.

In addition to investigating the position and motion of objects, your child will develop specific abilities and an understanding of scientific inquiry.

- Your child will become aware that observing carefully and then thinking and talking about observations are important parts of science.

- Your child will recognize that the more precisely she or he describes observations, the better others will understand the descriptions.

Talking with children about their experiences in science is a great way to renew your own sense of wonder and curiosity. Spend some time seeing ordinary things through the eyes of your child!

Sincerely,

Your Child's Teacher

Put-It-In-Position Cards

Put the brown crayon to the left and in back of C.Q.	Put the yellow crayon to the right and in front of C.Q.
Put the red crayon to the right and in back of C.Q.	Put the pink crayon to the left and in front of C.Q.
Put the orange crayon to the left and in back of C.Q.	Put the blue crayon to the right and in front of C.Q.
Put the black crayon to the right and in back of C.Q.	Put the green crayon to the right and in front of C.Q.
Put the purple crayon to the left and in front of C.Q.	Put the white crayon to the right and in back of C.Q.

Where From C.Q.?
Investigating Position and Motion

Put-It-In-Position
Record Page

Scientists _____

_____

_____

Crayon Color	Position of Crayon from C.Q.
crayon	
crayon	
crayon	
crayon	
crayon	
crayon	

Where From C.Q.?
Investigating Position and Motion

Find-The-Crab's-Name Page

H   M   B   H

B   N   E   P

U   C   R   O   R

P   Y   I

L   C   U

E   A

M   Z

How To Find the Crab's Name Page

Scientists _____

_____

_____

Directions

There are letters all around the crab.

Use the small paper clip to measure distance

from the ✚ on the crab to the letters of the crab's name.

◯ 2 ⊂▭⊃ s to the left of the crab.

1 ⊂▭⊃ in front of the crab.

◯ 3 ⊂▭⊃ s to the right of the crab.

3 ⊂▭⊃ s in back of the crab.

◯ 3 ⊂▭⊃ s to the left of the crab.

4 ⊂▭⊃ s in back of the crab.

◯ 1 ⊂▭⊃ to the left of the crab.

3 ⊂▭⊃ s in front of the crab.

◯ 1 ⊂▭⊃ to the right of the crab.

1 ⊂▭⊃ in back of the crab.

The crab's name is _____.

There are six more names for the crab.

- Can you find them?
- Can you write directions for finding each name?

More Than Direction
Investigating Position and Motion

BLM 5–2

Picture the Position Record Page

Scientists _____

_____

_____

Put yourself in the Norule picture.

- Circle the reference object in the question. (The reference object is already circled in question 1.)

- Pretend **YOU** are the reference object.

- Then **describe where** the is from you.

1. **YOU** are the  . Where is the from **YOU**?

2. **YOU** are the . Where is the  from **YOU**?

3. **YOU** are the . Where is the from **YOU**?

4. **YOU** are the . Where is the from **YOU**?

Picture the Position Record Page

Scientists _____

_____

_____

5. **YOU** are the . Where is the  from **YOU**?

6. **YOU** are the . Where is the from **YOU**?

7. **YOU** are the . Where is the  from **YOU**?

8. **YOU** are the  . Where is the  from **YOU**?

9. **YOU** are the  . Where is the  from **YOU**?

10. **YOU** are the 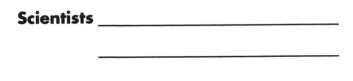 . Where is the  from **YOU**?

Picture the Position
Investigating Position and Motion

The Scwinch's Path

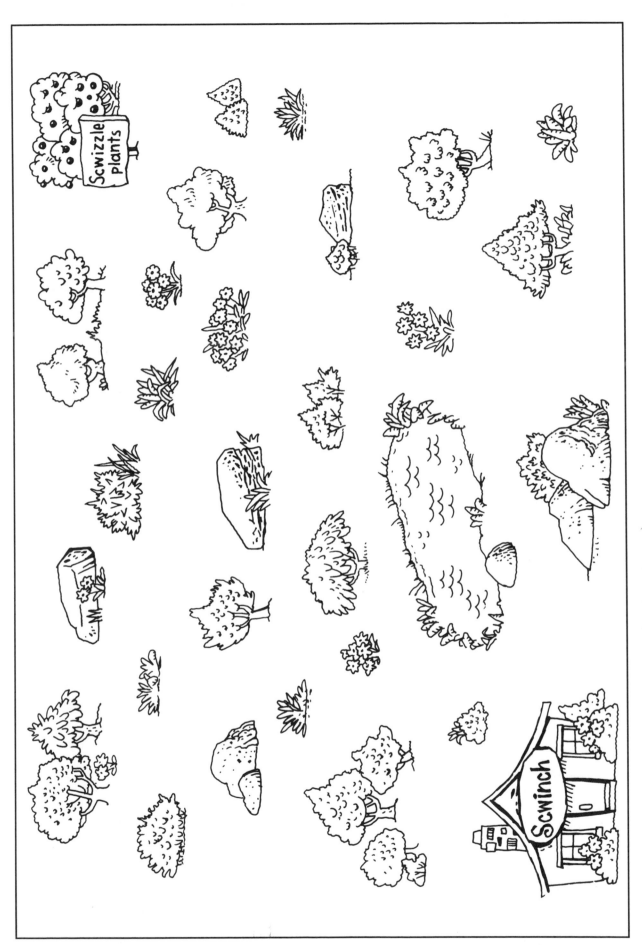

Motion and Paths
Investigating Position and Motion

Motion and Paths
Investigating Position and Motion

Describing Motion Record Page

Scientists _____

_____

_____

Investigation _____

1. Draw the ball's path and direction.

2. Describe the ball's motion.

3. Tell or draw something else that moves like this.

4. Change the ball's motion in some way.
   Describe how you changed it.

How Did It Move?
Investigating Position and Motion

Drop Races Record Page

Scientists _____

_____

_____

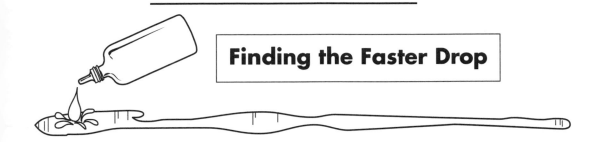

Finding the Faster Drop

1. We **guess** the _____ drop will be faster.

2. We **predict** the _____ drop will win the race because

_____

_____

_____

3. Show if the drop was faster **(F)** or slower **(S).**

RACE	BLUE DROP	YELLOW DROP
1		
2		
3		

4. We know the _____ drop was faster because _____

_____

_____

Drop Races Record Page

Finding the Fastest Drop

5. Team Formula

_____ blue drops + _____ yellow drops = green drops.

6. We predict the green drop will be

☐ Fastest

☐ Slowest

☐ Between fastest and slowest

Because _____

_____

_____

7. Show if the drop was fastest (F) or slowest (S), or between (B).

RACE	BLUE DROP	YELLOW DROP	GREEN DROP
1			
2			
3			

BOOKS

What Makes Things Move?
by Althea
Troll Associates, 1991.
ISBN: 0816721246. Nonfiction.
Grades K-3
> Discusses how both living and non-living things move or are moved.

Maps and Mazes: A First Guide to Mapmaking
by Gillian Chapman and Pam Robson
Millbrook Press, 1993.
ISBN: 1562944053. Nonfiction.
Grades 2-4
> A first guide to mapmaking.

My Map Book
by Sara Fanelli
Harper Collins Publishers, 1995.
ISBN: 0060264551. Nonfiction.
Grades K-3
> A collection of maps provides views of the owner's bedroom, school, playground, and other realms farther away.

As the Crow Flies
by Gail Hartman
Bradbury Press, 1991.
ISBN: 0027430057. Nonfiction.
Grade 2
> A look at different geographical areas from the perspective of an eagle, rabbit, crow, horse, and gull.

Measuring
by Sally Hewitt
Raintree Steck-Vaught, 1996.
ISBN: 0817241132. Nonfiction.
Grades 2-3
> Uses familiar objects and everyday situations to explore the world of measurement, weights, and size. Includes games and activities.

Mouse Views: What the Class Pet Saw
by Bruce McMillian
Holiday, 1993.
ISBN: 0823410080 Fiction
Grade 2
> The class pet wanders throughout the school.

The Way to Captain Yankee's
by Anne F. Rockwell
Macmillan, 1994.
ISBN: 0027772713. Fiction.
Grades K-2
> Miss Calico loses her way in going to visit Captain Yankee on Pebble Point, but her map helps her find his house in the end.

Long Way to a New Land
by Joan Sandin
Trophy, 1986.
ISBN: 0064441008. Fiction.
> Story of a Swedish family traveling to America in 1868. Students practice mapping skills in tracking the family's journey across the ocean and over land forms.
> *A Pegasus core title

Maps and Mapping
by Barbara Taylor
Kingfisher Books, 1993.
ISBN: 185697863X. Nonfiction.
Grades K-3
> Explains what maps are and how they are used, introduces symbols found on maps and describes how cartographers map the world. Includes related activities.

VHS (Videocassette)

The Magic School Bus Plays Ball
USA: Kid Vision, 1995. 30 minutes, animation.
ISBN: 1568325835
Explores basic principles of force and motion.

WEB SITES

VIRTUAL TOWN
http://wwwcsif.cs.ucdavis.edu/virttown/welcome.html
> Virtual Town is a World Wide Web index in the form of a small town. If you have a graphical browser, like Netscape TM, it shows the town as a map, with locations such as "Government Offices", "arcade," "post office," and so on, which are actually links to other pages full of links to other Web sites.

SUBWAY NAVIGATOR
http://metro.jussieu.fr:10001
    This site lets you check routes on subway sys-
    tems all over the world. Currently it includes,
    among other cities; New York, San Francisco,
    London, Washington, Milan, Paris, Marrseille,
    Toronto, Hong Kong, Tokyo, Montreal, Chicago,
    and Amsterdam. It not only gives you the route
    between your starting point and destination, it
    also gives you the estimated travel time.

WHAT DO MAPS SHOW—Teacher's background
http://info.er.usgs.gov/education/teacher/what-do-
    maps-show/index.html
    This site has comprehensive lesson plans and
    hands-on student activity sheets for students—
    all related to understanding maps. You can also
    download student map packets which you can
    print out for use with the lessons.